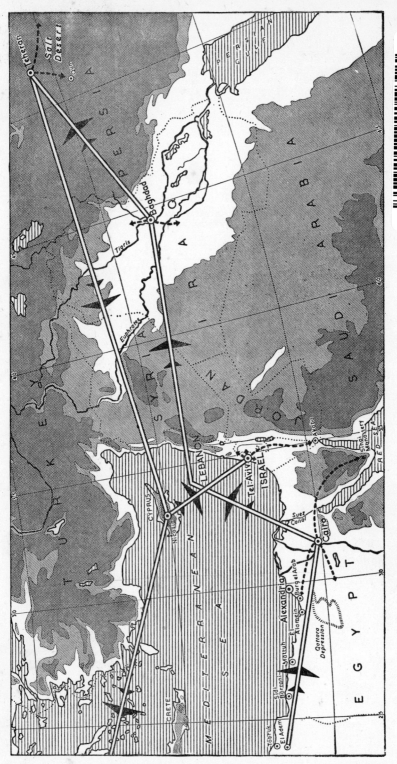

To Nell
from Auntie Jimmie.
August 1956.

# MEN AGAINST THE DESERT

*by the same author*

PROFILE OF SCIENCE

I. *Frontispiece* (overleaf)
DESERT CAVE-DWELLERS

# MEN AGAINST
# THE DESERT

## RITCHIE CALDER
### C.B.E.

Science Editor of the *News Chronicle*

Illustrations by Raymond S. Kleboe
staff-photographer of *Picture Post*
which co-operated in the expedition.

## GEORGE ALLEN & UNWIN LTD
RUSKIN HOUSE MUSEUM STREET LONDON

FIRST PUBLISHED IN 1951
SECOND IMPRESSION 1951
THIRD IMPRESSION 1952

PRINTED IN GREAT BRITAIN
*in 11-point Baskerville type*

BY C. TINLING AND CO., LTD.
LIVERPOOL, LONDON AND PRESCOT

# CONTENTS

# ILLUSTRATIONS

# PREFATORY LETTER TO THE AUTHOR

I AM grateful to you for having undertaken this journey on behalf of Unesco. The problem of developing for human use the vast desert surfaces of our planet, is one to which Unesco attaches great importance. Your articles from the desert have already found enthusiastic readers in many parts of the world. Your book will still further awaken public imagination to the challenge and the possibilities of the desert, and thus render a valuable international service. It should prove particularly useful in making the experience of scientists and engineers in the regions you visited known to readers in other countries where similar conditions exist.

J. TORRES BODET,
*Director-General, Unesco*

# ACKNOWLEDGEMENTS

I wish to thank Dr. Jaime Torres-Bodet, Director-General of Unesco, for the desert assignment and the facilities which his organisation provided.

My thanks are also due to the *News Chronicle* and the Editor, Mr. R. J. Cruikshank, for all the encouragement and support I received; for generously handing-over all rights in the original newspaper series to Unesco for world-wide dissemination, for issuing 20,000 maps and for coping with the thousands of letters from British schools.

The value of the mission was greatly enhanced by the pictorial record provided by *Picture Post* and I am personally grateful for the alacrity with which the Editor, Mr. Tom Hopkinson, offered cooperation.

Another 'sponsor' was Mr. Kingsley Martin, who promised, and provided, space in 'The New Statesman' for articles of assessment.

The success in schools was abetted by the willing cooperation of my colleagues of the United Kingdom Unesco Commission, particularly Sir John Maud, Permanent Secretary of the Ministry of Education, Mr. Ronald Gould, General Secretary of the National Union of Teachers, Dr. W. P. Alexander, Secretary of the Association of Education Committees, Mr. E. M. Hutchinson of the National Foundation for Adult Education, Mr. F. R. Cowell and Mr. William D. Pile.

I was able to travel so far and so fast only by the cordial help of the administrations in the nine countries I traversed and by the willing response to the exacting demands I made upon officials, scientists and new-made friends everywhere in the desert.

Finally, I want to thank my colleagues Miss Maisie Rosenthal, Mr. Hugh Baird and Mr. Tom Baistow who helped me to produce this completely new version of my journey in record time.

# HOW IT HAPPENED

THIS is the story of adventure in the deserts of North Africa and the Middle East. It deals with places which belong to the romances—with the Barbary Coast, once the haunt of pirates; with Foreign Legion outposts; with the desert encampments of the Bedouins; with the battlefields across which the Eighth Army fought its way from El Alamein to Tunis; with the Egypt of the Pharaohs; with the Sinai Desert where Moses and the Children of Israel wandered for forty years; with Baghdad and all its associations with Haroun Al Raschid and the Arabian Nights; with the salt deserts of Persia; with Cyprus and its connections with the Crusaders; and into Palestine. It links up with present times the great African domains—Carthage, Rome, Greece; and the ancient empires of the Middle East—Sumeria, Assyria, Babylon and Persia. It covers territory from which sprang three great religions, Jew, Christian and Mohammedan.

It was an adventure for me at least—and I hope that this book will help the reader to share my excitement of discovering strange characters, and stranger places; of crossing new horizons not only of an unfamiliar world but of knowledge; and of meeting a challenge to the imagination and abilities of man—no less than the recovery of the desert.

It began as a modest conception. I was asked by Unesco (United Nations Educational, Scientific and Cultural Organisation) to undertake, in my capacity as Science Editor of the News Chronicle, a tour of desert research stations to find out the kind of work which was being done in them; the kind of men and women who were devoting their lives to science in the desert; and the variety and scope of the problems which they were investigating.

'Modest'—but only in its original purpose, because geographically the possible range was enormous. The hot, dry

deserts of the world cover a third of the earth's surface. They
afflict five of the six inhabited continents, north and south of
the Equator. A one-man tour of these areas would have been
an enormous undertaking. But we decided to choose a sample
area which would give a cross-section of the problems. The
area we chose was the 'Classical Deserts', the area in which a
succession of civilisations, empires and cultures foundered in
their own dust—the deserts of North Africa and the Middle
East.

When we came to consider this area and what it meant, we
realised that the trip was assuming a different significance.
Here one could observe there not only what modern investi-
gators were doing but the warnings and lessons which the Lost
Civilisations had to offer. One could note What Is, What Was,
and What Can Be.

As we discussed it at the Unesco headquarters in Paris we
realised the extent of our own ignorance, or at least, unfamili-
arity with this area which impinged so much upon our culture
and so little upon our consciousness—and perhaps consciences.
That ignorance could be multiplied a millionfold in terms of
the peoples of the world, whom Unesco is seeking to inform
and instruct. If, as we hoped, science could do something
to recover the deserts, people everywhere ought to know the
nature and possibilities of those deserts.

So, what had begun as the immediate concern of the
Natural Sciences Division of Unesco became also an interest
of the Mass Communications Division which deals with press,
film and radio. How could the deserts be 'got across'? Gradually a scheme emerged by which, eventually, the story of this
journey was to be headlines, and a running commentary in
over 40 newspapers in 32 countries and to be carried on the
radio all over the world.

But there was another interested party—Education.
Through the U.K. National Co-operating Body for Education
this project was to reach, and be developed in, 15,000 British
schools. I was to be cheered on my way at various points-of-
departure in the desert by signals 'Another thousand schools
joined up today'. It was gratifying and encouraging because it

justified, or excused, my own schoolboyish zest for the adventure and my own wide-eyed naïveté in noticing things, which the usual textbooks (which I had not with me in the desert) would certainly have blurred or dismissed. If I had had my erudite friends to consult, I certainly would never have dared to have asked the apparently fatuous question 'Where did Hannibal get his elephants?' Yet that question started a train of enquiries and consequences which led me a long way from Hannibal and his elephants and has 'flummoxed' many of those erudite friends.

I repeat, it was an adventure. It released in me the schoolboy who is repressed in every grown-man. But it also had a serious adult significance which concerns, or should concern, every one of us: The population of the world is multiplying at an alarming rate—one more mouth-to-feed every one-and-a-half seconds. There are no virgin lands, like the new continents which fed the prolific Europe of the 19th century, to be broken by the plough. Indeed we are losing acres instead of gaining them. Lord Boyd Orr has said that to feed the world's population properly we shall have to double food-production by 1965. His emphasis is on 'properly' because half the existing population today does not get the food necessary for human well-being and, significantly, it is in those so-called backward areas where 'underprivilege' is most general that disturbance is becoming rife. It is too easy and too glib to label it with an 'ism'. Hunger is becoming articulate. Agitators may exploit the conditions; they do not create them.

In this precarious situation, the deserts which figure as blank spaces in the school-atlases become not a lesson in geography but in current affairs. The deserts might become the new lands which would help to relieve the pressure of population and the demand for food.

They are a challenge to the United Nations. If science can help, it is Unesco's job to mobilise the scientists for research. If there are methods which can be applied it is the concern of FAO—the Food and Agricultural Organisation—to see that they are made available. If development, beyond the means or competence of the desert countries, is needed there exists Technical Aid to under-developed Countries.

Meanwhile my Unesco assignment was to discover the Forgotten Men (and women) who in research stations throughout the desert are dwarfed but undaunted by the immensity of their task and to try to 'alert' the consciousness of ordinary people to the problems and possibilities of the deserts.

This was no elaborate expedition. It consisted only of Raymond Kleboe, the *Picture Post* photographer, and myself but we co-opted enthusiasts wherever we went. We had no equipment except the tools of our trade—a typewriter and recording machine in my case, and Kleboe's cameras—and the transportation which we coaxed or commandeered from the various authorities. I like to pretend that we hitch-hiked for 8,500 miles across the deserts. It was practically that—we never knew, until we had exercised our powers of persuasion on hard-pressed officials, how we were to get from one place to another. On one occasion, when I had been stranded for six days in the Western Desert, I actually 'thumbed' a lift in a motor-car over one of the worst stretches. On another, I hired taxis to take us round the Sinai Desert.

Perhaps the most rewarding experience was to come back to find how the thousands of schoolchildren had used the newspaper series in a lively experiment in project-teaching. And, above all, two letters by the same postal-delivery one of which described its success in a school for defective children and another from Balliol College, Oxford, saying that an expedition was being sent out to explore the Persian *qanats* which I had described (Chapter Nine). If the book can achieve that range of interest, it will have fulfilled its purpose. It is as much an adventure in education, as it is an adventure in travel.

# CHAPTER ONE

## INTO THE SAHARA

THE message which I received in the desert was: 'The White Father will meet you at the Well of Sefra on the night of the full moon at 1.30 ack emma.' I was to keep this strange appointment in the uncanniness of the Sahara night and to meet one of the most remarkable desert characters. But the story begins some time before in Algiers . . . .

The White Father had disappeared and Georges was in despair. As we waited for news, hour after hour, he paced up and down my hotel bedroom blaming himself and saying that he had killed the Father. All that we knew was that Père Harmel, Le Père Blanc, had left his hermitage in the Sahara to fly his own plane across the Atlas to Algiers, to pick us up and carry us a thousand miles into the desert to Beni Abbes, the Foreign Legion outpost.

His plane was long overdue and, in the meantime, a storm, terrifying in its violence, had broken over the Atlas; the weather had closed in 'round Algiers airport, making it impossible for aircraft to land. Georges had tried frantically to get news, telephoning towns and air strips between Geryville and Algiers, sending radio messages to desert posts and using even the desert 'grapevine', that mysterious system of communication by which the nomads somehow, without modern devices, get news rapidly from one desert encampment to another. Any news of the White Father would travel fast, for the Bedouins would be as concerned as we were lest anything had happened to him.

Georges' distress was natural. Father Harmel was his friend and out of friendship had agreed to put his own aeroplane at our disposal. If disaster had overtaken him, we would feel responsible for sacrificing one of the finest men of the desert.

Père Harmel's story is a strange one. His father was a textile manufacturer in Northern France, who sent his son to be educated at Bradford Technical College to train him for the business. When he finished, his accent was Yorkshire and his English was complicated with the queer jargon of the wool trade. He returned to France to do his military service, and chose the Air Force and won his wings as a pilot. When he left the Air Force, young Harmel, however, had a conscience-crisis. He did not want to go into the weaving business. He had a call to become a priest, and to dedicate himself not only to the Church but to a life of service to mankind. He might have chosen to become a Father Damien and minister to the lepers, but instead he chose the Sahara.

Young Harmel joined the Mission of Our Lady of Africa. This society is known under the name of Pères Blancs, or White Fathers. This was founded in 1868 by the first Arch-bishop of Algiers, Cardinal Lavigerie. The famine of 1867 had left a large number of Arab orphans and the society was formed for the care of these children. Missionary posts were established in the Sahara and the work has since been ex-tended into Central and East Africa. It had a heroic record in combating the evils of the slave trade and it had its many martyrs in the desert. So young Harmel forsook Western civi-lisation and went to North Africa. He was trained in the college of the White Fathers in Tunis, where Père Harmel became a master of Arabic.

He became to the desert Arabs a 'man of science' and science to them means not just what we call science but pro-ficiency in Arabic, in philosophy and in the Koran, which is the Bible and the law-book of the Mohammedans.

The young priest adopted the dress of the Arabs, the gan-doura, the long white cassock, and the burnoos, the flowing mantle and hood of the Bedouin, the tarbush or red felt fez, and wore the rosary and the Christian cross around his neck like the mesbaha of the marabouts, or Moslem holy men. Bearded, his face tanned by the desert sun, only the cross dis-tinguished him from the Arabs among whom he was to work for years, living their lives, sharing their camels and their caravans, their food and their tents, and serving them.

The desert Arab is a great arguer and will listen for hours to the rolling periods of his own or somebody else's voice. Huddled round the tamarisk fires at night, they argued the comparative religion of the Bible and the Koran with the White Father. Gradually he became a legend. An Arab in need through sickness or hunger would know that a message to the White Father would bring him many camel days across the desert to his succour. He became completely accepted— how completely anyone who knows the strictness with which Arab women have to veil and hide themselves can judge from the joke which the Arabs tell of Père Harmel. One day he entered an Arab settlement and immediately doors slammed and shutters were closed, and there was the scurry of the women into hiding. Then a woman's voice said 'It's all right. It isn't a man. It's the White Father.'

Then one day in 1942 the Allied Armies landed in North Africa. Out of the desert in his Arab garb came Father Harmel—to join the Free French Air Force. He became a combat officer, flying Spitfires with the Free French Squadron of the R.A.F. from Shoreham, Sussex. He ended the war as Squadron Leader Harmel, Distinguished Flying Cross. Then he forsook again the worldly fellowship of the Shoreham Mess and the daring brotherhood of Fighter Command and returned to his outpost in the desert. He took with him, however, one thing—an aeroplane—and he used it for his parochial duties in a parish as big as the British Isles. He started a flying club at Geryville and became its president.

It was his plane for which we were waiting with great anxiety. The flying experts in Algiers were extremely pessimistic about the fate of a light aircraft trying to cross the storm-besieged ramparts of the Atlas mountains.

Then we got the news from Geryville. The plane had made a forced landing on the Saharan side of the Atlas. The relief of Georges Cvijanovich, that lovable and emotional Slav, was something to be remembered.

The fact remained, however, that we had to get to Beni Abbes, and, if flying was impossible, the alternative was a 24-hour journey by train to Colomb Bechar, the southern terminus of the desert railway, and then 140 miles by goodness-knows-what transport across the desert. There was not a train for two days, but, however impatient we might be to get out into the Sahara, there was no choice. The storms which had prevented the plane getting through had brought snow to the Atlas Mountains and the passes were temporarily impassable, so that there was no possibility of going by road. In any event, the delay gave us a chance to see something of Algiers itself. Moreover, there was always Wallace.

Wallace was a great discovery. We ran into him in the unsuitable surroundings of an ultra-modern hotel in Algiers. 'Unsuitable' because it was rather like meeting an elephant at a tea-party. Wallace is huge—he must be 6½ ft. and built in proportion, with great buffalo shoulders and his bulk swathed in a tartan flannel shirt. I was first attracted to his corner by a voice. It was an emery paper voice, husky and gritty, as though sand had got into his larynx. Then there was his laugh, like the rumbling of a volcano. That was my first meeting with him in person, but I was to meet him as a jolly legend all over the desert. This geologist from Oklahoma is a character who has got into Arab lore.

Wallace is the prospector for an oil company—searching the desert for oil. Two-and-a-half years he, with a Swiss, an Italian, an Englishman and a Scotsman, had travelled backwards and forwards over the desert. Their caravan consisted of two huge trucks and a jeep. They had to carry not only their instruments and all the modern devices for geological exploration, but enough food and water and petrol, for months, in case they got stranded. They had to carry loads of spares because they reckoned to break at least twelve springs a month.

There is a true story—Wallace told me himself, but I was to hear it over and over again in the desert outposts—of how the party had been travelling across the sand desert for five days without seeing a soul. On the sixth day, in the great wastes as flat as the ocean, they saw a car coming over the horizon. They were so excited at the prospect of meeting

*Opposite :* FORT BENI ABB

GEORGES : The new "Foreign Legionnaire". Stateless scientist, Cvijanovich, recruited to desert research as geophysicist, at the Saharan fortress of Beni Abbes.

THE WHITE FATHER : Le Père Harmel (Sqn. Ldr., D.F.C.), flying Saharan missionary, indistinguishable except for the crucifix, from the Moslem Arabs whose garb he wears.

another human being that they charged ahead to meet him. They crashed head on!

That is Wallace, but it also is not Wallace. This 'rough-neck' is also a fine scientist and a philosopher. In the desert you get plenty of time and opportunity to philosophise. Where there is no roof but the stars, and not a sound, you can think. Wallace had done a lot of thinking about problems which were uncomplicated by the day's headlines. He had time to think about humanity and its future. Like everyone I met in the desert, he loved the desert, and it was breaking his heart that he was having to leave it and transfer his endless search for oil to the jungles of Equatorial Africa. Like many other people I met, he believed that the desert he knew could be made fruitful and come to the rescue of mankind.

It was Wallace who took us into the *kasbah*.

'Kasbah' originally meant fort, but in Algiers, as in other Europeanised North African towns, it has come to mean the Arab quarter. Although it is within a few yards of the fashionable shopping streets, one plunges into a completely different and sinister world outside the law, or at least outside any law except its own. Life is cheap in the *kasbah*.

The *kasbah* of Algiers is stacked on a steep mountain, rising above the harbour, which for centuries was the impregnable refuge of the Barbary Pirates—sea rovers, mainly 'Christian', operating under the protection of the Moslem Beys, and holding the shipping of the Mediterranean to ransom. The streets are staired passages, like dark gulleys up the mountainside. In either side there are dim, cave-like booths, lit by the glow of charcoal fires, or by olive-oil lamps, or, as a sign of affluence, by acetylene flares. Films like *Pepe Moko* have given some impression of the dim, dangerous mystery which is the warren of the *kasbah*, but even the dramatic resources of Hollywood fall short of the reality.

Anyone who goes into the *kasbah* goes at his own risk; there are no police to offer any protection. All the might of the Allied armies could not protect the soldiers or sailors who rashly ventured into its out-of-bounds dangers. The knife is

B

swift and silent, and the *kasbah* keeps its secrets. Around the great mosque in the *kasbah* is a sanctuary where anyone, whatever his crime, can claim immunity, but let him venture outside the sanctuary and French law will grab him. So there are outlaws who have lived in the sanctuary for years, setting up in business and plying trades. They are not sought by the police, because the police have found them long since; a policeman on his beat outside the sanctuary can look down on it and see the man he wants but cannot reach.

The *kasbah* itself is divided into quarters, round the *souks* or markets. Each *souk* has its own speciality—the food market, cloth market, the hardware market and so on. There is the Street of the Coppersmiths, loud with the clangour of hammers beating out coffee pots, teapots, chafing dishes and charcoal braziers. There is the Street of the Tailors, stitching the *serwals*, the wide, baggy breeches which both men and women wear, and very sensibly too, because in the hot desert the flapping trousers provide the draughts (and in the cold nights, warmth). There you can buy the *burnoos*, the heavy robe of camel-hair or goats-hair, with its hood to envelop the head in dust storms, or in the cold. The *burnoos* is an all-service garment. It is a dust sheet, an overcoat, a sleeping bag and a sort of one-man tent for the Arab squatting in the desert. It has no sleeves, just slits for the arms. Often it has hand-stitched designs, of which the basic design is usually the star sign of the Southern Cross, a design which originates with the Touaregs, that strange race of the Southern Sahara—'strange' because they are not Semites, like the Arabs or the Jews, or Hamites, like the black-skinned Africans. They may be some far older racial group, like the Basques. Even their religion, Mohammedan by conversion, has a character of its own. For instance, while the Arab insisted on his wives being veiled (in Algiers they show both eyes; in the Sahara only one), the male Touareg covers his face and the women go unveiled. Usually the Moslem woman has no rights and is the chattel of her husband (one of the difficulties of getting a reliable census of desert populations is that the Bedouin does not consider his wife sufficiently important to return her as a person). Among the Touaregs, however, the women choose their husbands and are a powerful matriarchal force.

The common dress of all Arabs is the *gandoura,* which you find under different names all over North Africa and the Middle East. It is a long shirt-like garment, which reaches down to the ankles. It is worn by both men and women and, while in the desert it is usually white, in many other parts it is highly colourful. The women in the *kasbah* wear what might be called an inverted apron. It is draped from the waist at the back but they gather it over the head and face like a shawl and veil, which completely covers their features.

Even in the daytime a visit to the *kasbah* is an adventurous experience. It is also highly colourful. One elbows one's way through the congested streets, crowded with Bedouins, Berbers, Moroccans, Jews and negroid types, because wanderers from all over North Africa find their way there to add to the overcrowded population, which no one has ever counted. Affluence and poverty jostle each other indiscriminately. There you will find a richly dressed *hadj,* with his yellow or gold turban, which means that he has made the pilgrimage to Mecca, and who will pay his alms to the innumerable beggars who expose their sores or lie limbless in the gutter. The *fez* or *tarbush,* the skull cap or inverted felt 'flower pot', is as common as the turban or as the *kfir,* the head-dress of the Eastern nomads, which is a muslin shawl held in place by ropes twined round the head. These ropes may be of twisted gold or silver thread, or just black cotton.

One thing which struck me looking at these Arab garments was the evidence of how much Western culture owes and admits to these Eastern peoples. They are a reminder that our religious and academic practices came from the desert region —and properly so, since in the expanses of the desert, under the arc of the sky and of the stars, men through the thousands of years have contemplated the infinite and have had time to philosophise. The *burnoos* is obviously the origin not only of the monk's frock and hood and of the clergyman's surplice, but of our academic robes. The *gandoura* is the cassock. The *tarbush,* which I suspect began as a prefabricated turban, gave us the mitre, the biretta and probably even the mortar-board. Further east, in Libya, I was to find that the Arabs in turn had borrowed from the Greeks and the Romans. The robes of the Western Desert Bedouins are essentially the Roman toga, and, indeed, they still call the pin which gathers them on the shoulder, 'the toga-pin'.

The *kasbah* at night, however, is not just an adventure—it is a hazard, and something to be attempted only with an escort like Wallace. It was not just his bulk, although, as he said, anyone attacking him would require, not a knife, but a harpoon, but because he was a character so well known and so well liked that, even in disreputable haunts, his company was the guarantee of our safety. He would bulldoze his way up the narrow alleys and we could go into booths and bistros where weapons would have been no protection. Indeed, when there was shouting and scuffling outside one place we visited, the appearance of Wallace was enough—clasp-knives snapped shut and daggers disappeared into the sleeveless robes. A husky order from Wallace and the gang scattered. Nevertheless, it was a relief to get back to the hotel.

The train left Algiers at 8.14 in the morning, a diesel-electric train, with comfortable compartments, and a dining-car, bound for Oran, which was not our destination. We got off at Perigaux, an orange town in the semi-arid region of Algiers, in the foothills of the Atlas, where the citrus groves are maintained by irrigation. At Perigaux we had to change to the desert railway, and we had to go into the market of the town to buy fruit and hard-boiled eggs, bread and water, for our long journey to Colomb Bechar. Some of the carriages on the desert train, which is steam driven, had hard wooden seats, but we travelled in upholstered comfort. In the next compartment was a *kaid*, or desert chieftain, and his two sons, returning to their encampments and their camels. This desert nobility was richly dressed, with gold-laced turbans, and smoking cigarettes from long silver holders. Their servants carried large, elegant suitcases, and installed a charcoal footwarmer against the rigours of the Atlas night.

For long distances the train ran along the side of the road, like a tramcar, and then crawled up through the passes into the snow. We ran through a blizzard and in the darkness we crossed a high plateau before we started dropping down the slopes into the Sahara. In the sleepless watches of the night, Georges told me his story.

Georges Cvijanovich is a young Yugoslav, a displaced person, with a refugee passport a yard long, who needs a visa or a permit not only to travel in and out of countries but to travel within a country. He was one of the first two 'men against the desert' whom I encountered. I had met him in Paris, in a restaurant on the Champs Elysees, together with Professor Menchikoff, who was born in Russia and was the founder and is still the director of the Centre of Saharan Research at Beni Abbes, to which we were travelling. Together we had planned this part of the trip over a Parisian lunch. Georges, who had been back in Paris collecting scientific equipment for his work as geo-physicist in the Sahara, had volunteered to be our escort, and with his packing-cases had gone on ahead by sea to Algiers, where we had joined him.

Georges' story is a tragedy of our day and generation. He had been a young student at Belgrade when the Germans occupied Yugoslavia and, like so many of his fellow students, he had 'taken to the woods' to serve with the forces of resistance. But Georges, who is deeply religious and loves his fellow men, was revolted by men's brutality to men. When he was ordered to act as executioner of a friend of his, and of his two children and of his wife who was expecting a baby, he refused and escaped to Vienna and later to Prague, where somehow he managed to continue his education as a science student. When the war ended he could not return to his distracted country because his father, a Government official, had been sentenced to death on a charge of favouring one section of Resistance against another. Instead he found his way to Paris, where he was joined by his mother and two brothers. Penniless he contrived, as a taxi driver and other things, to make not only a living for them but to continue his education for a degree at the Sorbonne. As a stateless person, however, he could not find a use for his scientific training until one day, in the Greek Orthodox Church in Paris, he met Professor Menchikoff who gave him employment in the Sahara.

Georges became infatuated with the desert and had been making lyrical promises that I would catch the infatuation too. Perhaps he was right. On this trip to Europe he had become engaged to a Swiss girl who was following him out into the desert to be married, as they have been since, by 'Le Capitaine', the commander of the fort at Beni Abbes.

At 8 o'clock in the morning the train wheezed to a standstill in the Sahara, at the terminus of Colomb Bechar.

Colomb Bechar is the military headquarters, the 'capital' of the military zone of the Sahara, an area considerably larger than France itself. Beyond it lies the emptiness of the desert. One has all the sense of a frontier town. From here start the great trans-Saharan trucks. Here is the depot of the troops. Here is the airfield from which the modern patrols go out to keep vigil over the desert; and here is the administrative centre of the social and economic life of the Sahara, presided over by Colonel Quenard.

I had been contemplating, with some misgivings, my interview with the Colonel. I was not sure how much sympathy a military 'brasshat' would have for a mission such as mine. My misgivings, however, were entirely misplaced. When I presented my credentials at the command post, I was received by the Colonel in a room which might have been the operations room of a military campaign. The walls were covered with large-scale maps of the Sahara, the kind of maps on which commanders dispose their forces. The Colonel himself was tall and rather stern-faced. When, however, I discussed with him the subject of desert reclamation, his face lit up and he became a burning enthusiast. He strode over to the wall map and began to describe his operation—not military dispositions but agricultural development areas—farming in the desert. I had expected difficulties but not of the kind I encountered. My travel arrangements on this long trip which was to take me as far east as Persia were tight.

He wanted me to see far more than my time would allow, and when I temporised, he immediately sent for his adjutant, ordered a command car to be put at our disposal, plotted my routes, sent signals to all the posts which he wanted me to visit and, where necessary, ordered a military escort—a not unnecessary precaution. Within a few hours we were on our way into the Sahara.

The command car was a powerful desert vehicle, covered with a hood but open to the elements—as we were to find to our discomfort later on. The first reminder that this was not going to be a pleasure trip came about twenty miles out of Colomb Bechar, when we pulled off the desert roads and turned into a square white desert fort guarded by Zouaves, the native troops. The Colonel's instructions were that we were to report here so that they could notify the next posts along the routes to watch out for us. This was a precaution in case misadventures overtook us.

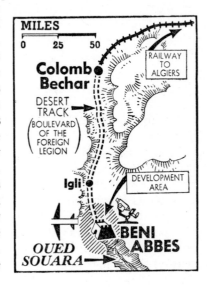

A little later, when we entered a defile—a grim, narrow path in the mountains beyond Fort Menouarar—we had an example of that kind of 'misadventure.' It was a monument to General Clavery and his party of Legionnaires, who 'died gloriously against the enemy in this place on the 8th December, 1928'. They had run into an ambush of a *rezzou*, or raiding party, which had descended from the mountains of Morocco on our right—and ominously near—to attack the caravan routes and capture slaves. That was a long time ago and the ill-defined borders betwen Morocco and Algeria are no longer harried by these marauders, who would, in any event, nowadays, be watched by air patrols. Georges, however, reminded me that that particular *rezzou* might have made our particular journey unnecessary. General Clavery had set out from Beni Abbes on that day in 1928 and with him should have travelled a young scientist who had been doing geological survey work in the Sahara. This scientist was Menchikoff who had escaped to North Africa with the Russian Black Sea Fleet and had turned Saharan geologist. At the last moment he changed his mind and did not accompany the party, which was wiped out. If he had died, there probably would have been no Centre of Saharan Research at Beni Abbes. For the Centre was the creation of Menchikoff, who, during these intervening years, had worked ceaselessly to bring together a group of scientists with proper equipment to tackle the many problems of the desert region.

Almost immediately all my illusions about the Sahara began to disappear. For one thing, even in the heat of mid-day, it was bitterly cold. The biting wind which blew through the command car chilled the marrow of one's bones. Then this was no great sand sea. We were travelling through bare, rugged mountains, now dropping into canyons, now travel-ling across great expanses of black rock, changing into flat plains of pebbles or sharp flinty gravel. We were in the region of *hammada,* or rocky desert. When we crossed stretches of sand, it crunched under our wheels and under our feet. It was crusted like a meringue, with a thin layer of sun-fused glass. The rocks themselves were black, enamelled by the heat of the sun.

This was 'The Boulevard of the Foreign Legion'. Just to prove it, there was a column set up in the naked expanse of the desert which testified that the 'Boulevard' had been built by the men of the Legion. To call it 'Boulevard' must have been some humorist's idea of a joke!

We were travelling the trail which was first beaten out by the pads of camels, then by the weary boots of marching men, and now by the enormous wheels of the trans-Saharan trucks and military cars like the one in which we were travelling. It twined and twisted through the passes and across the great expanses. It was a bone-jarring journey.

Then suddenly The Boulevard of the Foreign Legion plunged over the edge of beyond. There on the opposite side of a great canyon was the Fortress of Beni Abbes, on a ridge against mountainous sand-dunes.

'Look', cried Georges, pointing to what might have been an infant fortress on an adjoining ridge, 'that is the laboratory of the Centre of Saharan Research'.

This was what he had been promising me all the way from that Paris café on the Champs Elysées, through the snows of the Atlas Mountains and that hailstorm on the High Plateau, and across the cold desolation which had separated us from Colomb Bechar. This was Georges' homecoming, and in that first glimpse of white battlements tinted with the hues of the desert sunsets, I began to understand his infatuation with the desert. It was worth the trials of that journey of a thousand miles (or, by nomad reckoning, 40 camel-days) which we had covered from Algiers.

As we dropped over the edge of the precipitous valley, the heights cut out the sun but left us with a vivid sky in which the moon was rocking on its back.

Through the valley ran the Oued Souara. *Oued* is in French North Africa the word for *wadhi*, which through most of North Africa is the name for intermittent rivers—rivers which rush in spate once, twice or more times a year during the wet season and for the rest are just dry gullies. Even in the dusk, the Scorpion Oasis of Beni Abbes looked picturesque. It is called 'Scorpion', not because these vicious insects beset it, but because it is shaped like a scorpion, with a long tail stretching up the *oued*. Across the wide valley from the east came a camel caravan out of the Great Western Sand Desert. As we arrived in the heart of the oasis, the camel train was settling down for the night in the centre of the village. The grumbling, grunting camels were squatting down, the Arabs were building their brushwood fires and the Muezzin was calling the Faithful to prayer—'*Allah ila la Allah*'—and the cry was taken up and echoed along the valley.

We climbed to the opposite side of the canyon to the ridge on which stands the great citadel of Beni Abbes.

The vivacious young commander of Beni Abbes, Capitaine Raymond Clarisse, and his beautiful French wife, were waiting for us in the dusk at the fortress gate. On either side were the sentries, the *regibats,* troops recruited from the nomads of Mauretania. They were impressive figures in their uniforms of dark and light blue, with large blue turbans. At close quarters they were handsome, gentle creatures, but their reputation is rather like that of the Gurkhas of the British Army—absolutely loyal to their commander, absolutely ruthless in carrying out orders. One gesture from Le Capitaine and they would, without compunction, have slit our throats. Their reputation makes them dreaded by the outlaws of the desert and their loyalty makes them invaluable to anyone in charge of an isolated outpost such as Beni Abbes. Capitaine Clarisse and his wife both wore the *burnoos* with the hoods about their ears against the night cold. Like a good host and hostess, their welcome was as cordial as though we were old friends, as indeed Georges was.

Once inside the fortress the illusion of military might ended. It was a huge place, capable of housing a regiment. But today the citadel of Beni Abbes houses barely a platoon. Nowadays when the slave raiders from the mountains of Morocco no longer swoop down on the desert oases, Beni Abbes is an administrative headquarters for the civil affairs of an area as big as Yugoslavia, with a population of barely 20,000 who are living in near-starvation.

Capt. Clarisse showed me to my room—'cell' would be a more apt description. It was in the officers' quarters, with the battlements as my balcony. It was barely furnished and lit with oil lamps.

The captain invited us to dinner in his quarters, and his wife, gowned by Paris, served us a Parisian meal. After dinner we got down to business. I had already met Capt. Clarisse in his role as the military commander—in a film which I had seen in Algiers called 'The White Squadron', the story of the Camel Corps in an episode which is part of the history of the desert—the tribulations of the Arab squadron with its white officers, who went out to intercept the *rezzou* which had swept

down to catch slaves in the French Sudan and was intercepted
by the Camel Corps in the great sand dunes south of Beni
Abbes. Now I saw him as the administrator; he who embodies
in his person the entire Government of this huge area, glows
with excitement when he talks about his 'people' and his
plans. He just could not sit still as we talked of his schemes for
desert reclamation and for feeding his hungry people. Always
it was water, water, water, and the new crops and animals
which could be produced if only there were enough water.

In this military task he does not need the rifles of the
Foreign Legion or the death-for-glory exploits of The White
Squadron. He needs a new 'garrison'—the desert scientists
with their laboratory as their fortress.

Next day I met this scientific 'garrison'. A little group—a
biologist, a botanist, archaeologist and a physicist—formed
the permanent staff of the laboratory. But at various times
throughout the year they are reinforced by scientists from
Algiers University, from Paris, from Britain and from other
parts of the world, who make Beni Abbes and its laboratory
their base for the investigation of desert conditions.

The biologist would be more properly called an ecologist,
studying, as he does, not only the animals of the deserts and
the insects, but the whole nature of their environment. He is
Franklin Pierre, a red-headed Frenchman, who was assisted
by his young wife, a civil servant from Paris, who came to
Beni Abbes to be married by 'Le Capitaine' in the romantic
surroundings of the fortress and to receive the Church's bene-
diction from a desert priest who travelled 350 miles for the
ceremony.

With Franklin Pierre I ranged into the dunes of *Erg
Cheche,* which means the region of sand storms. Another
desert sortie which I made was with Philip Guinet, the
botanist. His concern is not only to explore the deserts and
find desert plants, but to discover from abroad useful plants
which might be introduced into the desert.

His job is to study plants of the *erg,* the sand desert, of the
*hammada,* the rocky desert, and of the *oueds.* The *erg* is sur-
prisingly rich in its variety of plants. There you find the best

adaptations to combat dryness. Tiny plants no bigger than a daisy may have roots twenty feet long. The tamarisks, which in the desert look like shrubs, are trees with roots 100 feet deep. The typical vegetation of the steppes on the edge of the desert are the cypress; the wild olives; the acacias; the jujubier, or lotus tree; and the armoise, the greyish fleshy plant on which the wandering flocks feed, and which smells like thyme. All these desert plants have a grey, ashen look, just as the plants of the Salt Desert have a blue look. One misses the fresh greenness, to which we, in wetter climates, are accustomed. Even someone like myself, completely ignorant of desert botany, must marvel at the extraordinary ebullience and persistence of nature. A tree will go down 100 feet to find water layers, a flower like the ephemeral flowers will grow from seed to blossom within a week, springing to life at the first skirmish of rain, living its brief vivid span and dying, leaving their seed as hostages to a climate in which they may never burgeon but in which they will clutch at the first excuse to live.

With Guinet, a handsome, enthusiastic, bearded youth, who looked like an artist from the Latin Quarter of Paris, I explored the experimental nurseries where desert plants are studied and where food plants from other parts of the world which might replace them are tested.

This garden was the creation of Madame Menchikoff, the wife of the professor, and had been in existence barely two years. When it was started it was just desert and rock. But I saw the miracle which water can work in desert sand—mandarin oranges as big as grapefruit, potatoes, cauliflowers, asparagus, etc. There were barley, broad beans, lemons, tomatoes, eucalyptus, peas. They can grow tomatoes, big juicy tomatoes, in two and a half months, lemons on the citrus trees. And nearby there was a military garden—a walled, irrigated and manured compound, where they grow poppies for morphine for use in the dispensary, which they are testing out as a cash crop. It is the harvest which they can sell to the druggists of Europe and get the money to buy wheat and peas for the Arabs. In this military garden, which supplies the fresh vegetables for the fortress, you will find most of the things you would find in a European garden, and many other things as well. This is all the result of just bringing water into the desert and using it for controlled irrigation. Curiously enough, one of the plagues of the desert farmer is our old familiar friend, the inevitable sparrow, who combines with the jerboa, the desert rat, to carry on a systematic pillage.

I went down into the wide oasis and saw the intensive farming of the Arabs themselves. Their main cultivation is, of course, the date palm, but they also grow vegetables and grain —wheat, oats and barley. Water comes down in spate in the wet seasons and spreads over the surrounding valley. There is also a continuous spring supply, which incidentally fills the garrison swimming pool all through the year before it runs off into the irrigation channels. The water is in the possession of the family of the *kaid*. He and his relatives, perhaps forty of them, are the water owners and they share it among themselves, and rent it under licence, as it were, to other landowners in the oasis who repay them with part of their crops. For the rest, most of the 1,100 people in the oasis are entirely dependent for their work and for their sustenance on the *kaid*, the water owners, and the landowners. There is no money for workers—they take it in kind. But the Europeans will assure you that whenever there is a shortage, the nobility, the *seigneurs*, will always see that there are fair shares and no one more than another will go hungry. That is as may be.

The apportioning of the water rights is itself a rite. There is a blind man, Taleb, who is a retainer of the *Kaid* family for the dispensation of the water. Taleb, the blind keeper of the water, lives in the *ksar*. The *ksar* is the native village of Beni Abbes. It is an extraordinary place. The streets are tunnels running underneath the living-rooms of the houses which are built of mud-bricks in solid rows. It is as intricate as a beehive. On the ground level are the sheds for the donkeys and other animals, including the chickens, and the people live above. Under this *ksar* runs a water supply channel. There in a dark corner sits Taleb on a stone worn concave by himself and his predecessors and by the village gossips who come and keep the old man company. He is the bailiff of a feudal system, a system which is sacrosanct under Koran law and cannot be interfered with by the French administration. Taleb, blindly measuring the amount of water which is to be supplied to each of the partner's fields, used to tip a copper pot into the wells. Into this copper pot he places a copper bowl with a hole in the bottom. The bowl sinks into the water slowly and the water comes up through the hole till, with a curious noise, like the gurgle of bathwater running out, the bowl sinks. That noise is the signal to old Taleb that the partner has had his fair share of water. He sends a messenger at once to the control point where that particular irrigation canal is then blocked and the entry to another canal is opened up, so that the spring water is diverted. All day he sits measuring out this water.

While the aristocracy—the *kaid* and his relatives—are Arabs, most of those who till the land of the oasis are the descendants of Negro slaves, slaves of the tribal nomads.

To have found Mr. Poueyto, the geologist, I would have had to have sent out search parties, because he and his wife had gone into the void on a six-months' geological exploration. They were doing the journey by camel and were pitching their tents wherever night might find them. They had left no postal address.

Georges Cvijanovich was the geo-physicist member of the team. In Paris he had been collecting his new equipment and all the way through the desert in the train and in the car he had been hugging like a bridal bouquet a delicate magnetometer. He would trust it to no one, not even to me. He had been boasting with great pride all the way about his magnetic laboratory and how he had excavated a cave in the sand and rock 60 feet beneath the Beni Abbes ridge. His new equipment included Geiger-counters for the study of radio-active materials in the desert and of the impact of the mysterious cosmic rays which bombard the earth from Space. He was extending his researches into atmospheric electricity and making fundamental studies of solar energy.

With all the excitement of a small boy wanting to show me his playroom, Georges took me across the sands to his cave. He wanted me to assist at the solemn ritual of installing his magnetometer. Then I saw stark and tearless tragedy. During his absence the termites had invaded the cave and had destroyed all the woodwork which had represented months of careful calculation and construction. Parts of the cave had collapsed and, in this isolation, where there are no skilled precision workers or laboratory assistants, Georges was faced with the personal drudgery of reconstruction before he could begin his scientific experiments.

Georges, however, like all desert scientists, has to be a fatalist. There, in the Sahara, time—like space—is immeasurable.

This tragedy did not spoil the jolly party which the staff of the laboratory had prepared for Georges' 'homecoming'. The 'boy' was sent down to the village to fetch draught wine from the general store. 'Boy' is a misnomer. He is a tall, black-bearded, swarthy, turbanned Arab, who has had 14 wives—not all at once, since Koranic law allows only four wives at a time. But it is quite easy to accumulate 14 wives, because all that is necessary is for the husband to say that he divorces his wife and her family has to take her back as a 'reject'. His current wife was the cook of the Centre who had prepared a massive *cous-cous*, a great chafing dish piled high with the pellets of ground wheat—a coarse semolina—which she had spent hours rubbing with her hand to the required size. Entombed in this were several chickens—the scraggy bald-necked chickens of the desert. This was served with scorching sauces, highly spiced, which burn the roof of your mouth if, as a novice, you mistake them for a kind of ketchup. Being a novice—and I was to learn sense in the next 10,000 miles—I thought we had to eat all this in case we should give offence to the kitchen, but I misunderstood the ritual of the *cous-cous*, because if you want to please the 'kitchen' you leave most of it. The remains are the perquisites of the kitchen staff and we could see all the relatives crowding round the fire in the courtyard to banquet on the left-overs.

In my subsequent journeyings amongst the Arabs, with that

hospitality to the stranger which is enjoined on them by the Koran, I was to enjoy (or perhaps 'endure' would be more appropriate) many a *cous-cous*—even to the ultimate test of the polite guest eating a sheep's eye which glared at me accusingly before I gulped it whole. This is the highest compliment a host can pay—solemnly to hand you the choicest tit-bit, and I did not risk offence by refusing it. I only discovered afterwards that I might have returned the compliment; a guest can honour his host by handing him back this tit-bit. While we were conducting the sortie into the Sahara from Beni Abbes, I received a bewildered message from London querying the mileages in my dispatches because they did not correspond to the map readings. The proper reply to that was that 'desert swanning' does not mean 'crow flying'. These innocent-looking arrows which appeared on the original chart of the journey represented arduous endurance tests which ultimately increased my mileage from a schedule of 5,500 to 15,500, of which 8,500 were by ground transport. What we foolishly forgot in planning the trip was that when one goes out into the desert one has to get back!

*Opposite :* TALEB, the blind water-keep and his donkey-boy.

WIND EROSION
Granite rock
sculptured b
sand blas
overlookin
Sinai Mona
tery in th
Mountains
the Ten Com
mandments.

WIND
EROSION :
Bare rocks—
the ham-
mada of
North Africa
—scrubbed
of soil by the
winds.

# CHAPTER TWO

## DESERT ROSES

AT high noon in the Sahara, I wore a windproof coat, a camel-hair undercoat, a Harris tweed suit, a polo-necked pullover and my winter underwear. I positively waddled when I walked, and still my teeth chattered. The major who was escorting us was wise. He wore a *burnoos*.

The winter cold—this was January—made Georges 'hopping mad'—for reasons other than physical discomfort. One of his ambitions was to get a photograph of *la dune blanche,* which means a sand dune covered with hoar frost. This is one of nature's trick effects, which can be seen at the sunrise only for a matter of seconds before the sun's rays wipe it off. Georges wanted a photograph as visible proof of the dew in the Sahara, or water in the 'arid' sand. *La dune blanche* is a clue to the mystery of one part of the water 'roundabout'— water-evaporation/re-condensation/water/wells—in which Georges, like many other scientists, believes there may be a practical way of abating the desert's thirst—by using dew. What annoyed him was when we got to Igli (70 miles north of Beni Abbes, where the Oued Guir joins the Oued Souara, and the two flow as an off-and-on river into the desert sands to the south) he found Sergeant Walter boasting that he had seen *la dune blanche* for a whole week—not for seconds but for ten minutes at a time.

Sergeant Walter is a typical 'man against the desert' who was caught by the lure of the Sahara. He was a giant German who, at 65, still had the poker-back of the Foreign Legionnaire. In 1913 he quarrelled with his father, left Germany and vanished into the Legion, among the men who chose to be forgotten, in those tough, violent days of 'Beau Geste'. All his life was spent in the desert, and when he was discharged from the Legion a few years ago he could not leave the Sahara. He became a solitary white man with a beret and apple-red

C

cheeks and a capacity for swilling *anisette,* the fire-water of the Legion. He chose the life of the 'Keeper of the Waters' at the barrage of Igli, looking after the flood waters and directing them into irrigation canals and basins where the water can linger a little longer and help to produce crops, instead of just letting it spread out and steam off.

Sergeant Walter produced for us a 'sand rose' as big as a flower show cauliflower. This is not a living plant but a beautiful cluster of sand crystals which grow into petals with veins like a flower petal. But these petals are as hard as glass. Georges could tell you that this 'rose' is another proof of the abundance of Saharan dew, because they are the result of the combined action of dew and sand and sun.

By this time our mission had become legendary—as the visit of the 'rain makers'. One Arab in the desert said I must be a very powerful *marabout,* or miracle man, because 'rain filled my footsteps'. (Sometimes it filled not only my footsteps but my boots as well.) We had brought the first rains to North Africa and the first snows to the Atlas, and places which get less than an annual average of two inches of rain in ten years had a millimetre or two as 'backsheesh' from our visit. At one place, under a cloudless sky, an Arab was frantically making irrigation canals. To our surprised interpreter, he said that a *crue* (or spate) was coming. He must have smelled it. Two hours later there piled up the blackest and most sinister thunderstorm I have ever seen, turning the daylight into night. In the open desert we only caught the flounce of its rain, but it broke over the mountains with a violence which was terrifying.

Desert lightning does extraordinary things. As the discharge strikes the dune it fuses the sand into glass. As a souvenir, I have a hollow glass tube of 'lightning glass', the sheath of a dagger of lightning.

The arid desert, however, cannot rely for its cultivation on wisps of rain, or even on the occasional visit of a Unesco 'rain maker'. There are three possible sources of water—the *wadhis* and the spates they bring down, which can be controlled and conserved; the underground water supplies which can be reached by wells and by artesian borings; and the dew.

I confess I did not realise the practical importance of the dew. We have, of course, in Britain the dew ponds of the Downs, but somehow one does not think of dew in the arid desert. Obviously, however, where you have such extremes of heat and cold, any moisture in the atmosphere (as distinct from the clouds) will be precipitated at night as dew. Under the fierce sun the dew, like rain, will be rapidly steamed-off—if it does not sink in in time. Inside the vast sand dunes, which look like the driest areas of all, there may be considerable quantities of this moisture. The dunes are like a sponge which can absorb water in two ways—surface rain or dew or by the upward seepage from the water-bearing porous rocks under-neath. This sponge effect can explain the *foggara,* the mine shafts which one sees in cliff faces and tunnelling under the dunes, from which a steady flow of water persists at all seasons. Indeed, the experimental gardens at Beni Abbes are irrigated by *foggara.* These tunnels go many miles into the earth, with vertical shafts at intervals, which provide air-holes, but were in origin the ancient engineers' ways of extracting the 'spoil' in excavating the tunnels. They are very ancient. Most of those which still survive were excavated by slaves when life was cheap. Now in the Sahara they are choking up because there are no slaves to be sacrificed in this way, and so far there is no mechanised equipment to do their work.

I shall return both to the question of dew and of the *foggara,* but I have to travel 10,000 miles before I am to meet them again.

I have said there were no slaves nowadays. There are—but it is not polite to call them so. In some parts of the desert there are slaves as completely bound to their masters as those in *Uncle Tom's Cabin. Kaids,* powerful in their isolation in some parts of the Sahara, claim the sanction of the Koran for slavery. An escaping slave will find it difficult to secure pro-tection even in White Man's law. There are, however, thousands of 'other' slaves, who come within the category which Colonel Quenard meant when he said 'In law we have freed the slaves—in fact there are still slaves in the Sahara'.

He explained: Land and water rights in the desert are in the hands of those *seigneurs,* the Arab *kaids* or chieftains, and their families. For them the landless, mainly of Negro extraction, work for their 'keep'—are paid in food, such as it is, and in shelter. Their overlords will see that except in common extremity they will not starve. But they cannot escape from their servitude except by trekking north into the Europeanised coastal belt to even greater misery in the ports which are already overcrowded with outcasts from the desert.

'Liberation can come only with the provision of new water supplies and the creation and settlement of new lands,' said Colonel Quenard. 'Then we can give a freer and fuller life to the people of the Sahara.'

One of my sorties was to Taghit. Taghit is a picture postcard version of the desert. It is called 'The Pearl of the Sahara'. To come upon it, as we did, from behind a range of mountains and to see it in glowing colours and shimmering heat was to experience an emotion which was a physical sensation; it made one's pulse quicken and one's heart leap. One felt 'This is Paradise.' It is a long oasis in a valley cradled in sand dunes. On one hilltop is a

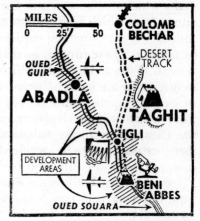

fairy-tale castle, which the Foreign Legion used as their watch tower. And on the other side is a large battlemented fortress, rose pink—not white, like Beni Abbes.

The Arabs, too, must think of it as a paradise, judging by the number of *marabouts,* or miniature white-domed temples, consecrated to the memory of Moslem saints. The sky-line is dotted with these *marabouts.* (*Marabout* can mean the place where a holy man is buried, or the place where the holy man lives, or the holy man himself.)

Paradise, indeed! Scenery does not feed the hungry. The

sole diet of the 3,000 human beings who live in the five villages
of this valley is dates and water. They never see bread; they
never have the comfort and consolation of the Arabs' sweet
tea, and they certainly never have meat. Their only product
is dates for which there is no trade to secure flour, sugar, tea
or other produce.

The oasis glitters in the sunlight. It looks as though it were
covered with snow; the water glitters but that 'snow' is simply
salt, ankle deep, and that water is brackish. The soil is practically useless; only the date palm, which ignores salt, can
survive. There is an idea of growing tobacco as a cash crop to
try to pay for imports into the valley. There is another idea of
poppy cultivation (which is also to be tried elsewhere in the
Sahara). But I found some misgivings among those who know
the people and the drabness and poverty of their lives about
this type of crop. If they once realised the escape which opium
from the poppy would provide, the problems of supervising
the crops and preventing drug addiction would be immense.

Abadla, sixty miles to the west, is a very different story. If
the approaches to Taghit stirred the pulse, those to the valley
of the Guir chilled the blood. To reach the valley one crosses
forbidding territory, through grim passes in the menacing
mountains and over a wilderness of slated greyness, a Gol-
gotha of desolation.

In my talk with Colonel Quenard at his headquarters at
Colomb Bechar, I had put my stock question, the childish but
always profitable query: 'Where did Hannibal get his
elephants?' Hannibal's elephants have always fascinated me
since I first encountered them in the classroom and learned
how they scared the Romans when they came trundling out
of the snows of the Alps through the backdoor into Italy. How
did he acquire those primitive 'tanks'? If he got them from
Asia (because some people suggest, against modern experience
in the Congo and in the zoos, that the African variety could
not have been tamed for battle purposes), how did he transport them? If they were marched from Asia, then the deserts
of the Middle East could not have been what they are today.
If, on the other hand, they were a tamed version of the African

species, brought from Central Africa, then the Sahara could
not have been what it is today—elephants could not have
traversed the distances between the oases. Or if he brought
them from Central Africa up the Nile Valley, then the
Libyan and Western deserts must have been different. Lastly,
if he found them in North Africa, then what is now desert
must have been forest and jungle. So whatever answers I get
to this question, the simple one is: The deserts were different.

Naturally I felt some nervousness in putting this 'quiz' to
an important military commander. I need not have worried,
however, because unwittingly I was 'on' Colonel Quenard's
pet subject. Without hesitation, he jumped from his chair,
crossed the room and pointed emphatically to a spot on the
map—'He got them from there'. 'There' was the Valley of
the Guir and he produced in support the evidence of Sueton-
ius Paulinus (the Roman General who defeated Boadicea).
Paulinus gave an account in A.D 47 of the Forest of the Guir
in which he described the elephants, lions and other wild
beasts which inhabited it. So, Colonel Quenard insisted, I
must go to the Guir. And I did.

At Fort Abadla, the command post for the Guir, I put the
same question to the commander. He was equally emphatic.
'And what happened to the forest?' I asked with a sweep of
my hand at the barren landscape around us. He led me to an
embrasure in the fortifications and pointed to a hilltop about
15 miles away. On this hilltop was a *marabout*, the tomb of
Sid Tayeb, a powerful Moslem holy man. 'There', he said,
'is your answer'. He thereupon produced from his archives
the legend of Sid Tayeb. Sid Tayeb was a miracle worker,
who might be called the St. Patrick of the Arabs. When he was
bitten by a horned viper in the Forest of Guir, he invoked
Allah and in his name cried 'I, Sid Tayeb, invite you to leave
at once the region of the Guir which I take under my protection'. He died, and six days afterwards, the legend records,
the elephants, lions and reptiles fled from the Guir into
oblivion. It was, however, the postscript of the legend which
really answered my question: 'And his followers, to whom he
bequeathed the forest, cut it down'.

'They cut it down'. That is the repeated tragedy, as I was to find, of the whole of North Africa and the Middle East—whether it was the followers of Sid Tayeb, destroying the Guir, or the Crusaders demolishing the oaks of the Enchanted Forest of Sharon in the Holy Land, or the Bedouins of Libya, who celebrated the victories of the Eighth Army over the Italians who had tyrannised over them, by hacking down or pulling up a million trees which the Italians had planted.

The Forest of the Guir, however, has not been lost for all time. It was a gratifying experience in this landscape of mountains which looked like slag heaps or pit bins, to go out from the military post and, over a ridge, to be dazzled by that 'English' greenness which is so rare in the desert. The greenery was a field of young wheat, and beside it the extensive market garden of the military post, with its prosperous plots of familiar back-garden vegetables—living proof that the Guir after all these centuries has not lost its fertility.

This valley stretches fifty miles northwards towards the Moroccan Mountains and is three miles broad on the average. It may have as many as five *crues* a year. That means that when the storms break over the Moroccan mountains the water rushes down in spate, a solid wall of water sometimes eight to nine feet high. This brings down not only the water which the thirsty desert needs, but rich silt, soil scoured off the mountains, which is deposited in a layer inches thick after each *crue* has subsided.

We drove across the basin of the Guir over a pavement as hard as concrete. The *crue* had passed a week before and this pavement—'crazy pavement' because it had cracked in shrinking—was sun-baked silt. One can lift the pieces up like tiles and I made a joking remark to one of the engineers that perhaps they could have an export trade in soil and ship these 'tiles' to other parts of the Sahara. But he pointed out this was not a joke, that they had in fact lifted the hardened silt of the valley and used it as soil for terraced gardens on higher ground.

The agricultural engineers of the *Society for Rural Amelioration* took us in charge. The Society's soil experts have made a survey of the Guir and have certified that by simple, modern measures they could bring into cultivation immediately 50,000 acres, and Colonel Quenard believes that the area could be extended and developed to supply all the wheat necessary for the population of the French Sahara. This area forms the tribal lands of the nomadic descendants of Sid Tayeb. As wandering tribes their practice is to plough and sow immediately after a *crue*; then to go off on their travels as herdsmen and return for the harvest and the threshing which they still do with flails and by winnowing—beating with sticks and letting the wind blow away the chaff from the grain.

The Society proposes, with the consent of the tribes, to develop a system of collective cultivation. It will provide the necessary machinery—heavy tractors, light tractors, disc-ploughs and machines for breaking the hard top-soil and cracking the sub-soil so that the *crue* waters can sink deeper into the ground and escape evaporation. In the centre of the valley there will be an agricultural experimental station where they will breed and select the best types of plants which will give the highest yield in this area.

With this modern equipment experts will plough and prepare the ground for all the tribesmen of the area. They will sow if necessary, and they will help in the harvesting and in the marketing. In return they will take a fraction of the cost. They are also considering secondary crops, like the poppy and cotton, not for export but for local wear. This scheme will do much to restore the usefulness of the Guir. It will be accompanied by systems of check dams—not barrages to store the water but weirs to brake the violence of the *crues* and to divert the water where it can be most useful. It must be accompanied also by conservation measures in the mountains, such as replanting of forests. This would prevent the eating away of the soil and the run-off of the water. It would, of course, reduce the amount of silt brought down but it would also extend the period of the flow of the *oued* by changing it from a drain into a stream.

North of Abadla we encountered something which to me

was a surprise—a coalmine in the Sahara. On the face of it, the mission, concerned with what can be done with the desert for food production, should not have been interested in coal, except as a piece of 'incidental intelligence.'

Fuel in the desert, however, is particularly relevant to food problems—not merely as a means of cooking, but, it is not extravagant to suggest, as a cause of the desert itself. Indeed, I would go as far as to say that energy is second only to water as a need for the recovery of the desert.

We occasionally encountered bands of women. Women, camels and donkeys are the beasts of burden of the Sahara. Women, without any protection, carry camel-loads of wood on their shoulders. You would see them filing over the dunes in the heat of the noon bent beneath their burdens. But if we tried to approach them, they would run off, staggering under their loads, in the opposite direction, gabbling like a flock of startled geese. Because they were clutching their load, they could not veil their faces from us Infidel males, so modesty and their religion compelled them to turn their backs on us and bolt. Our guide identified one party of about twenty of them by their dress as women of an oasis nearly forty miles away. In search of fuel, these women will trek for weeks across the deserts. When they find an odd tree or a clump of bushes, they will hack them and destroy them. Then they go on with the search until all of them can return together to their lords and masters with their back-breaking faggots. They have to find fuel to keep their families warm in the bitterly cold nights and to do their cooking. But every time they destroy a tree or pull up a bush, the desert wins another victory. That soil, which the vegetation has been holding together, breaks up and is snatched away by the wind to become drifting sand to add to a dune or to bury what had perhaps been a fertile garden.

Another enduring memory I have was the unexpected encounter with a nomad in his *burnoos* riding a nickel-plated bicycle over the trackless desert on his way to work in the Saharan coalmine at Kenadsa. Here, to the west of Colomb Bechar, is a coalmine—not a 'pit'—but a series of galleries driven into the decline of a seam from the outcrop on the hillside. The seam is only sixteen inches thick and the coal is inferior. But it serves for the power station which heats and lights Colomb Bechar, is used in the cement works and hauls the desert train to and from Perigaux. There is also, curiously enough, an export trade to Spain, a thousand miles across the Atlas. The mine employs 4,500 miners and produces 30,000 tons of coal a month. Absenteeism in this mine must be quite a problem, because the Arab miners are still desert wanderers. When a flood comes in the *oueds,* they trek back to their valleys to plough and sow their ancestral lands, return to the mine for the interval, and then go back again for the harvest.

There is another, much bigger seam of coal, both in extent and in thickness and much better in quality, about forty miles farther into the desert to the south. The development of this coalfield may be profoundly important in changing the character of the desert.

This coalfield and possibly the oilfield—for which our friend Wallace spent two and a half years looking in the Sahara—are reminders of the primeval forest and marshes which once covered this area in a long-past geological age. I do not think that there is any doubt that Wallace and his party did discover oil on their explorations, but his job is to find oil and keep his mouth shut.

He may be reticent about oil but he talks about every other subject under the sun—and I mean 'under the sun'—because one of his favourite themes was not oil but solar energy. Harnessing the sun may seem an eccentric idea to people living under the clouds of Britain, but out in the desert every scientist (including Wallace) is obsessed by the sun. They live with it. They see this vast amount of energy being squandered —1.35 kilowatts per square kilometre per second. Try working that out in terms of the expanse of the Sahara!

It has sometimes been suggested that perhaps atomic industrial power would prove its principal value not in the established industrial countries but in out-of-the-way places like the Sahara. It costs a fabulous amount even to bore a deep well in the desert because the boring equipment, with its oil-driven engines, needs a great deal of oil which has to be hauled over long distances. An atomic energy generator, once it was established, would not require this expensive transportation.

A pile, converting uranium into plutonium and releasing industrial energy in the process, would only rarely require fresh supplies of atomic fuel. One freight plane a year would probably be sufficient, since a piece of uranium no bigger than a matchbox is the fuel equivalent of 1,500 ten-ton trucks of coal or oil.

Tell the people in the desert that, they will point to the sun and say 'That's our atomic pile'. All the talk about the hydrogen bomb reminds us that constantly—for every instant of time, through all those multi-million years—the sun has been converting hydrogen atoms into helium and in the process producing a thousand times more energy released by breaking down uranium or plutonium.

In the desert, the scientists say 'If only the physicists, instead of trying to imitate the sun, for destructive purposes, would help us to harness the sun, we could have energy in plenty in the desert.'

Various methods have been tried, by using giant mirrors to focus the heat and various chemical solar-engines, but their efficiency is very low—like the one which I was to see later at Sidi Mesri in Tripolitania, which the Italians tried as a means of pumping water. They had to have an oil-engine as a stand-by, for use after dark, or for cloudy intervals. On the other hand, we know—although we do not know how it is done—that the green plant is a highly efficient solar engine, capturing the energy of the sun and converting it by photosynthesis into the food we eat. Using the by-products of atomic energy piles, the radio-isotopes, or radio-active elements, scientists today are trying to study this mechanism of photosynthesis. If they were to discover the mechanism by which the plants save up the energy in the hours of darkness, perhaps they could produce a solar accumulator which would store the intense sunlight.

As I remarked earlier, the question of finding fuel for the

desert is second only to the concern for finding water. If some-how scientists could make it unnecessary for these women to go on those long treks, destroying the sparse vegetation and encouraging such havoc of the soil by giving them some other means of cooking and of heating, they would be helping to stop the spread of the deserts.

If they had cheap energy, they could pump water to the higher desert areas—pump the Nile, for instance, to the thirsty desert plateau which stretches on either side of its valley. There would be cheap means of boring tube wells in the Sahara, going down to the deep underground water layers.

'We are walking on water', the Saharan scientists kept on insisting. They have reason to say so.

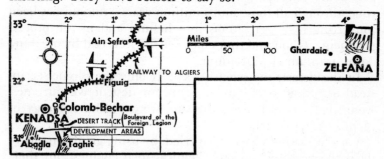

At Zelfana, some 400 miles east of Colomb Bechar, near Ghardaia, there is a new oasis, an island of cultivation in the desert, supplied from a well nearly 4,000 feet deep. Its im-portance, however, is much more than local, because it was the boring which, after many disappointments, proved the existence of a vast underground lake which stretches from the Atlas far into the Sahara and east to Gabes, on the coast of Tunisia.

This water-bearing layer is the *Albienne Nappe,* which as a source of water has been the guess and dream of geologists for over half a century. Many attempts have been made to tap it and prove its extent, but they all failed until the water gushed from Zelfana. The sinking here has proved that if one is prepared to go deep enough, there is plenty of water avail-able over large areas of the Sahara. Boring to great depths, however, needs energy, and oil for the drillers, as I have said, is expensive in these remote places. With cheap energy, anything might be possible, including boring to depths such as are now common in seeking oil, but depths at which, under present conditions, water would be as dear as oil.

# CHAPTER THREE

## THE MIRACLE MAN OF THE MARSH

THIS is the story of the Miracle Man of the Marsh who is having his marsh sucked away from underneath his feet. It is also the story of one of the most exciting and imaginative engineering projects which I was to meet on the whole of my trip.

All the same, much as I admired the cleverness of the scheme and realised the benefits which would come from it, I could not help feeling sorry for the Miracle Man who would wake up one fine morning and say 'Who's stolen my marsh?'

On the northern edge of the Sahara Desert is the Saharan Atlas. Between this range and the Tell Atlas, which fringes the Mediterranean coast, is the High Plateau, cupped in a saucer of mountains and in the centre of the saucer is the *Chott Ech Chergui.*

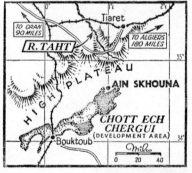

My imagination had been fired, before I left Algiers, by my discussions with M. Marcel Gautier, Chief of the Scientific Bureau of the Algerian Service of Colonisation and Hydraulics, who was principally responsible for the idea, but I caught the enthusiasm from M. C. Gaemeghling, the young engineer who is in charge of its development. M. Gaemeghling and his colleagues, Mr. G. Dreyfuss, M. L. Laurence Lesne, and M. P. Guillot, formed my escorting party for the exploration of the scheme.

A *chott* in French North Africa means a swamp and *chergui* means southern.

The basin of the *chott* is shown on the map as a lake a fifth of the size of France. It exists as a lake, however, only for a few brief spasms in the wet season when it becomes a shallow sea. Within a few days the sea has vanished and there remain treacherous, salty quicksands. The High Plateau which surrounds it is dreary, thirsty, hungry steppe-land. Its sparse vegetation consists mainly of *jujubiers,* or lotus trees, camel-thorns, *armoise,* the aromatic plant on which the sheep and goats feed, and esparto grass, the scattered clumps of which are harvested by the nomads by a simple process of pulling it out by the roots, bundling it on to camels, and carrying it to the warehouses scattered over the plateau where it is prepared for shipment generally to Scotland to be made into paper.

Being caught on this plateau at night is an experience which I have no desire to repeat. It was eerie in the extreme (apart from the physical hazards of driving blindly in a jeep along a doubtful track). When we had to stop, as we had to do frequently to wait for the jeep with the rest of the party which was following us, one had the uncanny feeling of being constantly spied upon and surrounded by voices.

Eyes of indistinguishable animals glinted in the darkness. *Jerboas,* or desert rats, bounded on their long hind legs like little kangaroos across the road, and there were rustlings and slitherings as though animals were stalking us. Voices which seemed very close to us were, in fact, ordinary conversations going on in Bedouin encampments ten miles or more away. Voices carry a long way in the cup of the High Plateau.

There was one particularly alarming episode when ahead of us appeared a ring of fires. We had no option but to go on —to charge through the fires in case it was an ambush. When we came abreast of the fires there was no one there. We stopped to investigate and found they were a series of burning bushes. While we were investigating, a white-hooded figure came galloping out of the night on a white horse. We were prepared to bolt for it, but he proved to be a friendly sheikh who merely wanted to know if we needed help. We then discovered the explanation of the fires. A shepherd following his usual practice had been setting fire to growing plants to keep himself warm in the miserably cold night. When one fire flags, he sets fire to the next bush. It is easier than cutting firewood, and although it is a bad thing to destroy the sparse vegetation of the desert, I could not blame him at that moment—I was shivering with cold myself.

When I recall that night I cannot be sure which made me more nervous—the mad drive in the jeep, which bucked like a broncho, lurched and listed to enormous pot-holes and nose-dived into *wadhis*, or the Witches' Sabbath of banshee noises.

In daylight when crossing the *chott* itself we had another strange encounter. A turbanned Negro, bare-foot, came running over the marsh to intercept our convoy. He brought us a summons from the Holy Man of the Marsh. 'Summons' may seem a strong word for a sociable invitation to drink ceremonial green tea. But it had the weight of a command for the engineers who were with me and who are planning to remove the marsh from under the feet of the Holy Man. The *marabout* or miracle man of *Ain Skhouna* (the hot Water Well), is a great power because he has mystical sanction over the people of an area which is as large as Belgium, and to offend him might be serious.

So we headed our jeeps across the marsh to the mound which stands near the Hot Spring and were received by the white-robed *marabout* surrounded by his brotherhood. He shook hands solemnly with each of us and kissed the tips of his fingers—that qualified welcome with which the Moslem receives the Infidel. Then he led us to his *marabout* (the holy place). The hut of sun-baked whitened bricks seemed much too small to receive our party.

This hut, however, was only the vestibule of a network of caves hollowed out of a chalk hill. He led us into a big cave —the Cave of Silent Thought—where he offered us tea. It was an elaborate ceremony in which he poured hot water into a teapot, added green tea-leaves and spoonfuls of sugar, poured a little into a cup, tasted it, made disapproving noises and poured it back in the teapot. This happened repeatedly. It was all part of the rite to show that no trouble was too much

MIRACLE MAN
OF THE MARSH: the marabout of Chott Ech Chergui holds court in his gypsum cave.

...AND THE ARAB MECHANIC, who is taking the marsh from underneath his feet.

MODERN:
Horse-
power
tractor,
disc-
plough-
ing on
contour.

in paying courtesy to a guest. When he was satisfied, he handed it out. It was so sweet one gulped it down like medicine, only to find that one was expected to have not only a second cup but a third cup. To the third cup he added mint. It was so sweet and syrupy and so heavily flavoured, one felt one was drinking liquid chewing gum. Courtesy, however, demanded that we drink it with loud sibilant sips—a sucking chorus led by the *marabout*—and ate with it hot fritters dipped in sugar.

After this silent ceremony we exchanged well-garnished compliments. We discovered later that the interpreter assured the *marabout* in Arabic that I brought to him the greetings of the entire United Nations and in his solemn reply he asked me to convey in return to the United Nations his blessings and salutations.

After this he dropped some of his solemnity and, like an excited chief, insisted on showing us the ramifications of his caves, including his sanctuary and a cave especially reserved for his cat, 'puss pussy'. Hewn deep in the gypsum, thrown up by the waters of the warm spring and hardened into solid rock, these halls were cool in summer and warm at night and in winter. There was nothing of the primitive cave-man about the comforts of this underground shelter.

Then he took us out to the open and showed us his camel-hair tent—a sort of low marquee—where his many wives, heavily veiled, and his many children, lived.

All this, I would remind you, took place in a great swamp, in a basin between the hills 2,500 feet above sea level. During the wet season, the surrounding mountains pour rivers into this catchment area, but such surface water coming into the *chott* disappears within a few days. What happens to the rest of the water?

M. Gautier surveyed this area by air. He recognised the *chott* as a great evaporation pan, from which the sun steamed off the water. Something more was happening, however. Measurements showed that the *chott* throughout the year was evaporating more than the surface water. Water was coming up from the porous rocks 200 feet below and was being evaporated.

D

Calculations could show, or at least estimate, how much of the water from the surrounding mountains ran into the area with the surface water, and how much was soaked into the artesian layers. Allowing for the immediate loss through evaporation in the mountains and for the tiny fraction of water given back by the widely scattered wells, including the hot spring of *Ain Skhouna* itself, the rest must be going into a vast reservoir replenished annually by 1,000 million cubic yards of water, and much of that was seeping up into the evaporation pan and being lost as atmospheric moisture.

Here, for anyone with scientific knowledge and above all with scientific imagination, was a challenge. How could this water which was being lost be recovered and put to use?

The surface water of the *chott* is useless, because the soil is very salty and the water is contaminated by it. The artesian waters, however, are relatively fresh.

Ranging in a jeep over the dubious roads of the *chott* from the village of scientists at *Ain Skhouna*, I saw the drillings, forty of them, which have proved the existence and the range of the underground lake of fresh water. Water was spouting in the desert.

It is estimated that the water evaporated from the underground lake is equivalent to about six inches of rain a year and that there is an annual inflow into the porous rocks of thirty cubic yards per second. The water-experts reckon that it should be possible, therefore, to withdraw twenty to twenty-four cubic yards per second throughout the year. That over an area this size is a lot of water.

To understand the scheme it is necessary to understand the geography of Algeria. It is divided into five regions: (1) the coastal plains; (2) the Northern Atlas; (3) the *Hautes Plaines,* or High Plateau; (4) the Saharan Atlas; and (5) *Le Vrai Sahare* or True Desert.

The High Plateau extends from Morocco to Tunisia. It is essentially an area of esparto grass and mutton. Esparto is a wild crop. The sheep are poor specimens and the Arab khaki-coloured cattle are scraggy, because, apart from the sparse pastures, they have to make long journeys of perhaps two or three days between the water-holes. There are primitive attempts at grain-growing, but there is not much encourage-ment, since every year there is a risk of drought and one harvest in five, at least, is a complete fiasco.

One of the objects of the *Chott Ech Chergui* operation is to supply sweet water for the flocks and herds of the plateau. It aims to provide water-holes and wells at comfortable dis-tances. Already there are forty tube wells, experimental borings to secure scientific data, providing water for the nomads, and when other pumping stations are installed, they will be able to extend drinking water all over the plateau.

The second purpose is a major scheme which may change the entire character of Algeria. It is designed to attack the underground 'lake' and transport the water from this high level reservoir through the mountains to the Algerian coastal plains and the fertile land on the coastal slopes of the Atlas. These plains, between Oran and Algiers, are semi-arid but fertile, and with irrigation from an all-the-year round water supply could increase their productivity abundantly.

The geography of the area lends itself to another develop-ment. Most of the fertile land of the coastal belt is below 600 feet altitude, but the water supply under the *chott* is 2,100 feet above sea level, so that there is a 1,500 feet head of water which can be used for hydro-electric generation and could supply all the electricity needed in Algeria. The extension of the scheme would be a great system linking the whole country, so that the water power which is 'borrowed' from the High Plateau will be returned to it as electric power.

I toured the *chott* to see the experimental borings and the scientific researches which are being carried out to make the scheme 'water-tight' and also the laboratories in the scientific oasis of *Ain Skhouna*. This is a township, of trim bungalows and communal and administrative buildings, which has been erected in this drab area to provide reasonable comfort for the scientific pioneers.

Already two of the artesian wells which are spouting have been linked to a pumping station which is part of the first stage of the scheme which is planned to develop in phases.

Each phase is self-contained but would add up into the final elaborate scheme which will cost at least £120,000,000.

The first phase will be to pump the water along open pre-fabricated tunnels, with relay pumps at intervals to lift it into the headwaters of the Taht. This is an intermittent river which flows northwards into the coastal plain. Already they are constructing a barrage at Uses le Duc, which I visited, to contain the floods of the Taht and serve at the same time as one of the system of barrages which will harness the water from the *chott*.

The final phase will be to drive tunnels through the mountains into the 'sump' of the artesian layer, under the *chott*, and drain it towards the north. This will have the effect of dropping the water level so that the water will not percolate upwards into the evaporation pan which is the great *Chott Ech Chegui*. They will, however, be draining off only part of the annual intake of the layer—an important consideration since any drastic draw-off would affect the existing natural springs. Indeed, all they will be using, in effect, is that water which now is wasted by evaporation. Here is a plan which proposes to supply the water and energy needs of a vast territory merely by using the sweat of the soil.

The opposite of this—and it shows the agile imagination of the French scientists in Algiers who are tackling the Algerian problems—is a scheme which I later visited at Relizane in the coastal plain. Here there is a marsh which, at sea level, cannot have the hydro-electric usefulness of the *chott* at 2,100 feet. But is a large, reedy, mosquito-dangerous waste in an area which is otherwise fertile. This swamp is fed by water-bearing underground layers in the surrounding hills. What they are doing there is to sink a ring of wells into these porous seams above the level of the marsh to catch and draw off the water in them before it reaches the marsh. This trapped water is then diverted to irrigate the good land, and the marsh, bereft of its water, will be recovered for agricultural purposes.

In the operation of this project I saw a remarkable drilling equipment, sinking a well to a depth of 300 feet, but using a boring-bit which had tungsten teeth and which cut a pillar of

rock one metre wide. Then, like a dentist's pliers extracting
a giant's tooth, it pulls up this core, which looks like a massive
Corinthian pillar of hard limestone rock.

On the edge of the High Plateau where, in the south-west,
the mountains slope away into the Sahara is Ain Sefra—the
Well of Sefra. There, on the night of the full moon at 1.30
ack emma, I met the White Father.

We met round a charcoal stove where a queer group was
drinking coffee in the chill moonlight. One was a burly under-
officer of the Foreign Legion. He greeted me affably in
Cockney English but he pulled the hood of his *burnoos* over
his head and strode off into the Nowhere before I had an
opportunity, even if I could have taken it, of discovering his
story. The others, as far as I could judge, were all Arabs in
motley garments, from the usual *burnoos* to the unmistakable
remains of a G.I.'s overcoat. They were having a lively and,
for Arabs, an unusually hilarious conversation, and the centre
of it all was a sheikh-like figure. By his crucifix and by that
alone, I identified him as the White Father.

This was the meeting which I had wanted and which had
been postponed by the flying weather over the Atlas. We had
twice tried to make contact in the desert, and this rendezvous
at Sefra was the outcome.

As the desert train drew out from the halt at Ain Sefra,
I clambered on and pulled the White Father after me. He
wanted to go north to recover his stranded plane and fly it
back to Geryville and I wanted to know a great deal more
about Father Harmel and his desert 'parish'. We talked all
through the night and all the way to Algiers. There I had to
catch the airliner to Tunis on the next stage of my desert
journey.

# CHAPTER FOUR

# BY TRAMWAY ACROSS HISTORY

A TRAMWAY runs from Tunis to Carthage and in thirty minutes you can traverse 3,000 years—provided, of course, that you have someone like M. Charles Saumagne to help you forget that Carthage now disguises its ancient history behind the elegant pretentiousness of ultra-modern villas and is now a dormitory suburb of the capital.

Charles Saumagne was one of my lucky accidents. 'Accident' because he did not figure in the schedule and 'lucky' because he was extremely knowledgeable on the problems with which

I was concerned and because he has a rich Gallic sense of humour. And there is no greater boon in desert travel than a companion with a sense of humour.

M. Saumagne was the Inspector-General of Tunisian Administration — the permanent head of the Civil Service. He came to my rescue when I found myself in difficulties. The Tunisian Administration had planned for me a tour which would have taken me three times as long as my available time would allow. When I explained my predicament to the Inspector-General, he swept aside his desk papers and said: 'I shall come with you myself'. So did M. Tixeront, Chief Engineer of the Hydraulic Service, and Madame Claude-Alain of the Residency Staff. With three such 'bottleneck' busters and informed guides,

54

I managed to do all that had been planned in a third of the time.

M. Saumagne by great good luck was an archaeological enthusiast and an authority on ancient Carthage, and really to understand the desert problems of Tunisia, one has to go back to Carthage. What happened in the past 3,000 years has a profound bearing on what is happening today and can happen in the future.

So, rather like a Bank Holiday excursion to Hampstead Heath or Hampton Court, we 'did' Carthage. With a sweep of his hand Saumagne abolished Modern Carthage, which might be any Mediterranean seaside resort, and plunged into the past. To discover Phoenician Carthage, of 3,000 years ago, we had to go round the back streets and find, tucked away among the suburban houses, the Graveyard of the Infant Sacrifices—all that remains of the Phoenicians.

When the Romans razed the proud city to the ground and symbolically drove a plough through the ruins, they did a thorough job. They destroyed an empire which dated back to the 16th century B.C., when the Sidonians, from the Levant, established a trading station on this site. Then Carthage was founded about 850 B.C. by Tyrian emigrants led by Elissa, fleeing from the tyranny of her brother Pygmalion—Elissa who was to be known in history and legend and in Virgil (in the *Aeneid*) as *Dido,* which means 'the fugitive'. This empire was to clash with the aspirations of Rome. Its military and mercantile power was to be destroyed in the First and Second Punic Wars. It was, however, the Third Punic War which had significance from my mission.

When the sea-supremacy of Carthage was destroyed and it was deprived of its means of trading, the Carthaginians had to turn their energies and enterprise from trade to farming and concentrate on the development of the hinterland. Their peaceful expansion into their own undeveloped territory was their undoing. They were so successful as agriculturalists (and the system of cultivation which they adapted to the needs of North Africa was to be the basis of Roman and Greek farming there for centuries afterwards) that when a Roman

mission of inquiry went over to intercede in a local quarrel
between Carthage and its neighbour Numidia, Cato the
Elder, who was a member of that mission, was so impressed
by the prosperity of Carthage that he vowed its destruction.
When in the Senate he declaimed *Delenda est Carthago*
(Carthage must be destroyed), he waved a bunch of figs.
Carthage by its productiveness had become not a military
threat to Rome, but an economic threat to the great land-
owning class which was beginning to develop in Italy.
'Carthage must be destroyed' because it was doing too well.
Ironically, they who lived by the plough must perish by the
plough. The pretext was found for the Third Punic War,
that ancient piece of Hitlerism.

With dramatic vividness, Saumagne reconstructed the last
days of Phoenician Carthage, ending in a description of how
the mothers, besieged in the Temple of Eshmun on the hilltop, took their children and flung them over the parapets
into the flames of their city, before they perished themselves.

When Julius Caesar, pursuing the last supporters of
Pompey, reached Carthage, he found the city still in ruins
and housing the scattered remains of the Punic population.
He decided to restore it as a Roman colony and under the
Caesars Carthage was turned to splendour and magnificence.
The ruins which people see today are the remains of Roman
Carthage, with its amphitheatre, its temples, its baths and
villas, the Carthage which, in its turn, was to be ravaged by
the Vandals, restored by Belisarius and finally destroyed by
Hassan the Arab in A.D. 697.

Even the ruins were robbed in the successive centuries.
Carthage was 'cannibalised' by later generations to provide
the prefabricated columns and masonry for other cities. One
finds all over Tunisia—in the Mohammedans' holy city of
Kairouan and in Sbeitla—magnificent pillars of Greek,
Italian and Egyptian marble and granite, but you find them
also in the great buildings of Europe including the leaning
tower of Pisa. The sea laps the foundations of Carthage and it
was easy for ships to ground themselves on to the beach, put

out gang-planks, and roll the Glory of Rome ignominiously into their holds.

History—and, of course, it is basically Roman—has always excused the fate of Carthage by dwelling (as the defenders of the Conquistadores do in the case of the Aztecs of Mexico) on the horrors of human sacrifice. We hear of the horrible rites of sacrifice to Baal-Ammon, or Moloch, and how, in Carthage, children were placed in his bronze arms and slipped one by one into the furnace in an orgy of fanaticism.

In that Children's Graveyard in the suburban backyard of Carthage, M. Saumagne challenged this reading of history. There, in five layers of excavations, are the urns which were supposed to contain the bones and ashes of the first-born sons of every family whom Moloch demanded as sacrifice. In the bottom layers, of the early primitive days of Carthage, the urns unmistakably contain infant remains. But in the upper layers of the era when Rome was venting vengeance, the urns contain not human remains but the ashes of birds and animals. The Carthaginians had come to love their children more than their blood-thirsty gods.

Returning from this graveyard we climbed a hill above Carthage to another graveyard—the cemetery of the French soldiers who died in the Tunisian campaign of the Second World War. From here one can look two ways. One can look down on the ruins which have suffered the plunders of two thousand years; one can look the other way over the low ground which stretches away to the hills and one can see another kind of plunder—the plunder of the soil.

The road to Tunis runs across solid ground which was once an arm of the sea, and which made Carthage not a promontory, as it is today, but a peninsula; the silt of eroded soil has filled in the natural moat.

At sunset, as the sun's rays slanted across the landscape, a queer thing happened. We saw the outlines of the long-forgotten Roman fields reappear as shadows—geometrical squares, which once bounded acres of wheat and barley.

In the middle of the night, our party set off from Tunis on its long journey into the hinterland of Tunisia, which was to take us to the holy city of the Moslems, Kairouan, to Sbeitla, the lost city of the Byzantines, to Kasserine Gap of faithful memory in the Second World War, to the Garden of the Hesperides and the cave dwellings of Matmata. The first stretch of our journey took us in the darkness across the neck of Cape Bon in which were bottled up the last of the Axis troops in the decisive campaign which won North Africa. I confess that in the darkness and at that hour M. Saumagne's round-by-round description of the final battle was of less concern to me than the prospect of breakfast.

In the first streaks of dawn we pulled up in an Arab village in front of a lighted booth. It was the Tunisian equivalent of a fish and chip shop, but what was frying was not fish. An Arab, seated like a Buddha on a high altar among fumes, not of incense, but of olive oil, with a bowl of stiff batter beside him and a pan of boiling oil between his knees, was making *ftaier*. These were pancakes or fritters which he slapped into the boiling fat. Smothering them in sugar he plonked them, fried fish fashion, into an Arab newspaper. We ate this oily indelicacy—printers ink and all—with relish and then adjourned to a nearby coffee bar, where, with the Arab workmen, we washed the oil down with syrupy coffee. In retrospect this meal makes me feel queasy. In Tunisia it set me up for the day.

Eighty miles south of Tunis we reached Enfidaville, familiar place-name in war-time bulletins, where we turned away from the coast westwards into the semi-arid region with about ten inches mean annual rainfall but with prolonged droughts. This is the country of cactus hedges which act as windbreaks; the fleshy leaves are feed for camels and sheep, and when the crops fail the 'figs' become a staple diet for human beings. Most of the land here is farmed under the *Maharsa Contract*. This contract, which derives from an old Turkish practice, is a form of share cropping. The land-owner calls in the Arab and says 'Plant my land with olives'. The trees take 15 years to reach maturity, but in that time the Arab works the land, plants barley and other crops in between the trees and the landlord makes advances to tide the peasants over. At the end of 15 years there is an olive grove, the products of which are divided between the landlord and the cultivators.

We passed over wide stretches of wilderness, which, as M. Tixeront pointed out, was good land which ought to be under cultivation, but which has fallen out of commission under the Moslem equivalent of mortmain, by which property is bequeathed inalienably to the Church. These 'Allah's Acres' are the common lands of the nomads. They cannot be properly farmed and remain for the most part as scrub pasture. This is only one of the many problems of land tenure which keeps barren the good earth of North Africa.

By midday we had got to Kairouan where in the *souk*, or market, jostled by camels, bumped by donkeys and badgered by beggars and by traders, we had more fritters, more printer's ink and more syrupy coffee. Kairouan is one of the principal holy cities of Islam. It is a town of 500 mosques. Most of them are small 'chapels' dedicated to some holy man or sect, but others are very large and the greatest of all is the Great Mosque of Akba, the Companion of Mohammed in the *Hegira* (the Prophet's flight from Mecca to Medina in A.D. 622, from which dates the Moslem calendar).

According to the legend, Akba, at the head of his desert cavaliers, who conquered North Africa, arrived in a 'sinister desert', where they made their camp in the solitude. His followers protested because there was no water, to which Akba replied 'We must rest here and even here found a city, for that is the wish of Allah'. They objected that there was neither water to drink nor timber, nor stone to build such a city. Akba silenced them with the words 'Allah will provide'. The next day a scout returned saying that a greyhound had found water. (That well, with a camel padding round and round turning a water-winch, is still giving water.) On the second day the scouts who crossed the ridge found a forest and on the third day an avalanche of rocks—'An army of stone on the march came down from the mountains'. The only weakness of the last miracle is that Kairouan is almost entirely constructed of brick and such masonry as there is has been 'borrowed' ready cut from Carthage and elsewhere. In the Great Mosque, for instance, are great blocks of masonry with the Roman inscriptions upside down, beside marble and granite pillars from Italy, Egypt and Greece, tanding on their heads.

To get into the mosque we had to have a permit, which took us not only into the vast courtyard but inside the mosque itself. This, like the temple in which Jesus taught, is not only a Church but a university. We had to take off our shoes and our escort carefully removed all the prayer mats from our path, in case we defiled them by our Infidel footsteps.

There, under the great dome, squatting in circles on mats on the floor, were the students reciting the Koran and questioning their teachers. These were the doctors and lawyers and philosophers of the future, for the Koran is the source of everything.

From the vaulted roof hung massive chandeliers of what looked like jam-jars, the olive-oil lamps which must have given the mosque, in the past, a light much preferable to the glaring light of naked electric light bulbs which now dangle.

As we left we were nearly trampled by the stampede of students who, like any schoolboys (and of course there were no girls) at 'break', came careering out with their satchels.

Kairouan has massive fortifications, surrounded as it always has been by desert and exposed always to the danger of attack from continuously revolting desert tribes. The minaret of the mosque, with its 129 steps, was used not only by the *muezzin*, calling the Faithful to prayer, but as a look-out, maintaining a continual vigil over the threatening desert.

Between Kairouan and Sbeitla, the capital which it replaced when the Byzantine power crumbled, we had a twentieth century mishap—just a burst tyre, but in a stretch of desert as grim as we were to see anywhere. It was spectacular erosion, as though the world had burst at the seams, exposing narrow crevasses and gaping canyons, and hanging precipices which one felt even an echo would bring down on one's head.

In the midst of this desolation was an Arab farmer and his family. The youngest could not have been more than about six, but he was hanging on to the handles of a primitive plough pulled by an ass. His eldest brother had a plough yoked to a camel and a third brother was belabouring a decrepit horse. The father was scattering sparse handfuls of seed and the children were ploughing it in with shallow wooden shares. It was all very boisterous, with the children goading their motley team into a race. They would charge along, until in collision with a boulder the youngsters would take a toss, like being thrown over the handle-bars of a bicycle. All the time they were marking out, in the desert, the exact proportion of the ancient Roman fields, such as we had seen in the sunset at Carthage. Where they learned their geometry lesson, nobody knows.

Sbeitla is a ruined city as eloquent in its way as Pompeii. Its stones, which have a golden glow in the sunlight, have a deep meaning for our day and generation. Sbeitla (Sufetula) was the capital of Gregory, the Patrician of Africa, who rebelled against the Byzantine Emperor in the 7th century A.D. He was the Viceroy at Carthage, but Constantinople was a long way away and he made the excuse of a religious quarrel to declare himself 'Emperor of Africa.' Just in case, however, the Emperor could muster enough strength to deal with him and send ships against him, he withdrew from Carthage and retreated into the desert, where he counted on the support of the Berbers. By some stupendous effort he managed to drag inland massive columns and stone blocks from Carthage and, with local stone, began to build himself a capital. At first the Berbers accepted his rule, but when the flying columns of the Arabs from the east invaded Tunisia, the Berbers joined forces with them and Gregory was slain under the walls of his capital in A.D. 648.

It is not, however, the fate of an Emperor which makes Sbeitla significant. Among all the pomp and circumstance of Byzantine basilicas, theatres and baths, are impressive villas, but their walls are blind. There are no doors or windows. Each villa was a fort within which, with the patios, their fishponds and their baths, the occupants lived in a perpetual state of siege. Access was by wooden ladders which were withdrawn. Above the living-rooms were stores for olives and grain and food generally—supplies enough for a beleaguered garrison. Miles away across the desert were the fortified farmhouses, within the circumference of which Sbeitla once sustained farms to feed its population. But when the desert people made war on Sbeitla, the farmers abandoned their fields and with-drew to the city forts. Cultivation became furtive. Desert marched in.

Later in Tripolitania I was to see the modern version of this process. Mussolini, with his dreams of an African empire and the restoration of the Glory that was Rome, set out to establish Italian colonies. These were designed for the exclu sive benefit of Italians to the ruthless exclusion of the Arab population. When he decided to drive the Arabs deeper into the desert, he dropped Senussi chieftains out of aeroplanes as a warning to others. He sealed with cement the wells, near the coastal belt, which were necessary to the nomads for watering their camels and their flocks, and thus he drove them deeper into the thirstlands. Then he created settlements and, for the wrong motives but with the right methods, the Italians ex-tended cultivation deeper and deeper into the desert. Each settlement was based on its own water supply and had archi-tecturally imposing centres, which embraced the amenities of an entire communal life. Out from these centres radiated the farms, with their irrigation systems.

When Italian power collapsed in Cyrenaica, the Italian colonies withdrew and abandoned their settlements to the Arabs. In Tripolitania, where the conflict between Arab and Italian was not so violent, the British caretaker government which administered the territory liberated by the Eighth Army managed to give the Italian settlers a measure of security and they continued in possession. No Italian, how-ever, could feel entirely secure on the desert fringe and they began to withdraw from their farms on the circumference and retreat towards the settlement centre. It is the story of Sbeitla repeated in modern times, because the desert is liable to march in again. Only by hard work and constant farming can the outer defences of desert farmland be maintained.

The Kasserine Gap was a battlefield. It gives access through the mountains to the west into Algeria. It was here, in the North African campaign, that the fresh American troops, the Task Force which had come from the U.S.A. without battle experience, were advancing into Tunisia in a manoeuvre to join up with the Eighth Army coming from the south. Here in the gap it met the unbridled ferocity of a counter-offensive by Rommel's hardened veterans. It was a serious reverse but in turn the Axis troops were to be hammered and battered in those same confines and forced to withdraw towards their final collapse.

Kasserine is once again a battlefield. Huge machines are deployed across the valley. Men are 'digging in'. Searchlights illumine the African night. But Kasserine is not a military centre now. It is the key centre of the Lost Land. The machines are not tanks but tractors. Men are digging not trenches but ditches. They are working night shifts, by searchlight, to make the most of the equipment they have got.

The development of Kasserine was not an afterthought of the Second World War. Its origins, strangely enough, were in the Spanish Civil War. After the defeat of the Republicans, refugees poured into North Africa. Work had to be found for them and the Tunisian administration decided on a big project of public works as a form of active relief. Three thousand refugees were sent to Kasserine, which in Roman times had been an important grain centre, as the amphitheatres testify. Their job was to build a barrage dam across the gorge of the *Oued Dherb*. At first it was just an encampment, but these Spaniards borrowed an idea from the Berbers. They became modern troglodytes, or cavemen, dug themselves caves in the limestone cliffs and created for themselves commodious and comfortable homes. It is a freak of time to stand in an amphitheatre 2,000 years old, and look through the span of a modern suspension bridge at families of cave dwellers.

Most of the Spaniards have now dispersed—Fascism from

which they had escaped overtook them in the war, and scattered them. About fifty Spanish families remain, but Kasserine will always have a lingering Spanish quality. I ate Spanish food in a Spanish restaurant, in an oil lamp village which will presently become a township of an area with a population of about 16,000 settled on new land which has been recovered from the desert.

From the dam on the *Oued Dherb* run concrete canals to supply the valley. A modern aqueduct in the form of an impressive suspension bridge carries the water across the gorge. A new irrigation system at Kasserine already irrigates more than 5,000 acres. Green fields are creeping over the one-time battlefield.

Kasserine will always remain a particularly vivid memory. M. Saumagne and I went out into the desert plateau above the gap. It was moonlight. We looked down on the barren lands that were coming to life. M. Saumagne who, up to now, had been a rollicking companion, was very serious and powerfully moved. 'Tell me,' he said, 'that there are in the world ten men who believe that the desert can be made to blossom —ten men who believe that we can redeem the stupidities of mankind—and I shall die happy.'

Meeting M. Saumagne was an experience I would not have missed. This tall, broad-built Frenchman is a rare character by any standards. As a youth at the university in Paris he was a student of classical history who decided that the destiny of the French empire depended on colonial agrarian reform, so he joined the Colonial administration to devote his life to North Africa. He kept his interest in antiquities, but his obsession was people, and the land to feed the people. He had the soul of a pioneer and the job of an administrator. His dreams had to be docketed in files. He had to struggle with law, finance, politics and the Koran. He became an expert Arab scholar, to argue with the people for their own good. He became a time-biding statesman, never losing sight of his objectives, in spite of every frustration and disappointment. He was a human fraction—a humanist divided by an administrator. As we stood above the Kasserine Gap he was within a

ADVANCING DUNES : Overshadowing a desert fort.
Overwhelming a desert township.

DUNE FIXING : Planting dess grass in a network of squares to prevent sand drift.

FIXED DUN
Egg-timer s
is changed i
soil by irri
tion in t
years (sam
trays at o
year interva

few months of his retirement and only now was his life's work beginning to blossom.

Later, at Castilia, he was to have another emotional moment and he was to see the birth of an oasis for which he had worked for 25 years. Castilia is unlikely to be found on any map. It lies between Toseur and De Gache. These are two old natural oases, but Castilia is a man-made oasis. An artesian well had been sunk to great depth and the water was bubbling up at a rate of three gallons per second, filling the reservoir and flowing in irrigation canals to fields which were already planted with crops and which in years to come will be a great grove of date palms. When a quarter of a century ago M. Saumagne went into the south to survey this future oasis, he had to go with soldiers with rifles to protect him from the indignation of the Arabs who saw in this scheme, to benefit them, merely an invasion of their ancient rights. Reluctantly, and with inexhaustible patience, he had to wait until persuasion, necessity and the passage of time would make it possible for him to give the 'all clear' to M. Tixeront and his colleagues of the Hydraulic Service. In time the oasis of Castilia will extend eastwards and westwards along the margin of the great salt marsh of Djerid, to link up with Toseur and De Gache. De Gache is a very fertile oasis with banana plantations and orchards. And from the marginal soil they can harvest ten to twelve crops of esparto grass a year. Toseur is a honeymoon town, a romantic excursion into the desert. It, too, is richly productive.

On the way back to Gafsa—because the road across the marsh which we would have to take to reach Gabes had become a death trap, not of quicksand but of quicksalt—we visited the Oasis of the Seven Wells. These, again, are Roman in origin, and are now being cleaned out and linked to give ample water to another desert strip. We passed Metlaoui, the area of the phosphate mines which yield a million tons a year for chemical fertilisers and are apparently inexhaustible.

Gafsa, the Tunisians claim, was the Garden of the Hesperides. It was here, if you believe them and the myth, that the golden apples were guarded by the Three Maidens 'who live far away

E

in the west where the sun sets.' The golden apples grew on a tree, guarded by Ladon, the ever-watchful dragon, which Hercules as his Eleventh Labour slew, to steal the apples.

Certainly I saw a sunset over Gafsa, which was so exquisitely beautiful that it could colour any legend, and I saw 'golden apples' in abundance. And who can say that grenadines were not the Golden Apples of Hercules? Moreover, Gafsa even as it is today—perhaps more so as it is today—is an oasis, the fertility of which would seem mythical if it were not actual. This oasis provides a living for 12,000 peole. For those who think of an oasis as a water-hole and a few palm trees, this may seem surprising, but it certainly is an oasis, an island of well-watered cultivation in a desert with less than five inches of rain. Here are great olive groves, citrus orchards, apricot gardens, fields of wheat and barley, market gardens with endless varieties of vegetables, and every square foot of it depends on irrigation. There are natural springs, artesian gushers and wells from which water has to be pumped from a depth of 100 feet. The water runs in a natural stream, or in prefabricated concrete channels, like mile-long water troughs, or is siphoned in pipes from one reservoir to another. The dragons who today guard the fruits of the Hesperides are the hydraulic engineers.

If Gafsa is an exaggerated idea of an oasis, Gabes—the Oasis of a Million Palms—must be more so. Gabes, on the sea coast, is another of those war-time headlines. But today the fight is to extend further and further the water supplies which are all that is necessary to bring the wilderness around to life. Here, there is a co-operative of all the private individuals who own the water, and by literally pooling their water resources they are creating new land. One of the problems is salt in the soil. This is a problem which I was to encounter a hundred times on my journey. Just as at Taghit in the Sahara the fault is not in the water which has only a small fraction of salt, nor in the original soil. It is the continuous accumulation, by evaporation, of the tiny fractions of salt. At Gabes they can overcome this by carrying the water in low concrete aqueducts over the salty soil to the fresh soil, or they can, as they are doing in one large experimental plot, use the night flow of water which is not required for systematic irrigation to flush the salt out of the fields. This they do by digging a broad, deep trench —a moat—around the field and draining the salt into the trench.

Without being very optimistic about our reception, M. Saumagne, that veteran in Arab relations, agreed that we should go up into the Matmata Mountains to find the Moslem cave-dwellers. His doubts were due to the fact that Moslems regard any approach to their women folk as a cardinal sin and any intrusion into the intimacy of their homes as a violation. Among the cave-dwellers, however, the situation is even more delicate. If you *walk* on their homes it is desecration, and since their homes are concealed in the mountains, there is every risk of running innocently into trouble. That is what happened.

We had made a perilous climb, by car, up mountain roads, carved like shelves out of the cliff face and leading apparently to nowhere. Every time we came to a cross roads, they seemed to point in another direction to where we had come from, until we decided that the French military had elaborate deception plans just to confuse people in this military zone which was part of the famous system of Mareth Line defences. Anyway, we seemed to go round and round the Matmata as though we were on a scenic railway—only the descents were much more unnerving than any Giant Racer I have ever been on.

Finding the caves was all the more difficult because they are completely camouflaged in the mountains. One can look at a mountain riddled like a rabbit warren with caves and still not spot them. They are not, like the conventional idea of a cave, driven horizontally into a hill. They are pits sunk vertically. When one gets 'wise to them', one begins to spot the manure heap which adjoins a concealed cave. According to our bearings we had arrived at the troglodyte settlement, but we could not quite reconcile the cavemen with an elegant modern school, until M. Saumagne assured us that this was the cave-boys' school, and a very lively and highly intelligent boy with a roguish face under his turban confirmed this.

Like a boy scout doing his good deed for the day, he volunteered to take us to the cave. We were scrambling up a rocky hillside when we were stopped by a bellowing behind us and a furious figure, his robes flying in the wind and his beard bristling with fury, chased after us, followed by a group of supporters. M. Saumagne said in French 'This is it' and went forward to parley with them. Right enough we were threatened with a riot, because at that moment we were walking on the fellow's cave. There was nothing to do but beat a retreat, although, as far as the Moslem was concerned, the damage was done.

Meanwhile, 'Young Alfie', as I nicknamed our 'Boy Scout', had gone off to find his father to try to get us out of trouble. His father turned out to be a very broad-minded and friendly Berber who, in his own language, of course, said 'Don't pay any attention to that silly old so-and-so. He's a crank.' And then made the surprising offer to show us his own cave.

He took us to a hole in the ground which must have been at least thirty feet deep and about twenty feet in diameter. It was like looking down into the well of a block of flats. He led us to the concealed entrance where we entered by an incline and found ourselves surrounded by a series of living-rooms occupied by his several wives and their several families. He took us into their sleeping quarters which were tidy and comfortable, with lurid lithographs of Arab 'pin-up girls'. Then he took us into their kitchen-cum-living-room where a fire of sweet-scented shrubs was burning and where one of his wives and the children were squatting, preparing a highly-spiced meal. He took us into the lofts where he stored his grain and into his olive store deep in luscious black olives, and then to his olive presses. Great Ali Baba jars, man-high, stood filled with the season's olive oil.

In the centre of the courtyard, to catch any downpour, was a water cistern, but most of the water has to be carried from the wells. He took us to see his donkeys in their underground stables, and M. Saumagne played Santa Claus to a swarm of mahogany coloured youngsters whose mothers were unabashedly showing their faces unveiled and grinning with pride as their son or stepson (as the case might be), 'Young Alfie', aired his school-room French.

It was all very jolly, very friendly and sociable.

Another tortuous and torturing journey took us to Medenine, an extraordinary town of beehive houses. These houses were a series of mud huts, each with its arched roof, stacked one on top of another like the cells of a beehive, and climbing, rather perilously it seemed, to the height of a five- or six-storey tenement. We had been told that we would find the old town of Medenine deserted—a new town of modern houses has grown up in the vicinity. On the contrary, however, we found the streets and the houses teeming. But it was a town without women, and as we went around, avoiding kneeling camels and jostling camel drivers, we discovered the explanation! The old town is a *caravanserai*, a free lodging-house, for the Arabs from the mountains when they come in to sell their produce. They come without their women and just 'park' in the beehive town.

During the last stages of our journey through the barren mountains of Southern Tunisia, Madame Claude-Alain was in great pain. She tried to disguise it and to be her vivacious, helpful self, but she was obviously in great distress and my medicine chest, with its antidotes for snake bites, malaria and even cholera, could not muster an aspirin to relieve her headaches.

It was then that M. Saumagne, by way of explanation, took me aside and told me her story. She was 'Claude', one of the heroic women leaders of Resistance, first in Tunisia and later in France itself. When France collapsed, North Africa, through Vichy, fell under Axis domination. 'Claude' and many others went underground. Her activities were discovered and she was later imprisoned in Morocco, where for a year they tried to compel her to disclose her comrades. Then, thinking they had tamed her, they released her, but leaving her two sons and three daughters in Tunisia, she was deported to France and again escaped into the underground. She joined the forces of the *Maquis*. On one dangerous mission she was caught by the Gestapo and put to torture, of which she still bears the scars. Among other things, she was exposed to kleig lights for 48 sleepless hours. With the fierce rays of the lamps beating down on her, she was questioned by relays of interrogators, trying to break her resolution and force her to disclose information which might have meant death, or worse, for hundreds of her associates. They did not succeed, but as a result the nerves of her eyes were damaged and the exposure to the desert sun on our journey had tortured them afresh with the pain of 'a hundred toothaches'.

That was the least of it. The physical pain had revived the nightmares—all the hours of mental anguish in 14 different prisons and those culminating horrors in the death camp at Ravensbrück, where under deferred sentence of execution she had to watch her friends one by one being taken off to their death. Then, in the confusion of the last days of Hitler, she escaped. She wears the ribbon of the Legion of Honour.

M. Saumagne decided that Madame Claude-Alain must be got back to Tunis, although it meant travelling all through the night. They were going back north; we were heading south. So, on the Mareth Line, we parted company.

# CHAPTER FIVE

# DESERT DERBY WINNERS

BETWEEN the French Tricolour at Ben Gardane and the Union Jack at Zuara, there is a No Man's Land over forty miles broad, once the fortified zone. Now there is a vista of wrecked pillboxes and Italian forts, the shattered remains of Mussolini's military defences. Rather ridiculously, in the middle of this desolation, and divided by a mile or two, are two Customs barriers, straddling the road with nothingness stretching on either side—rather like a garden gate without a fence.

Nevertheless we were stopped at the French post for quite a time because the French driver did not have his entry papers to Tripolitania and the Arab guard had a long telephone discussion with his Arab opposite number at the British post. The guardroom was full of Bedouins who had obviously called in for a morning chat and a glass of coffee, all very nice and sociable, like a most exotic country inn. While we were waiting I took a childish delight in going behind the guardhouse, stepping over into Tripolitania and stepping back again!

Our car was cursorily searched for contraband and with many salaams the guard solemnly raised the barrier and we drove through. It was like something out of a Marx Brothers film—for a thousand miles to the south the border is wide open and the authorities on both sides recognise that camel trains of smugglers are continuously crossing to and fro. Indeed, the main commerce of both Ben Gardane and Zuara is contraband.

Before we got to the British barrier we were met by the Controller of Agriculture, Mr. W. J. V. Taylor, and the Political Officer from Zuara, and I was solemnly handed over by the French authorities to the British authorities.

If it were not brutal, it might be a good thing to leave Zuara as a living object lesson of man's wilfulness and thoughtlessness. Before one's eyes one sees the fate which overtook the ancient civilisations that foundered in a sea of dust of their own creation. It was the same fate which threatened the capital, modern Tripoli, forty years ago when the sand-sea crept to the city centre and lapped at the steps of the Turkish Residency. In Zuara one could see sand dunes advancing house-high into the town, abandoned homes with just the roofs showing, palm trees which look like shrubs, and a large warehouse, the walls of which were bulldozed by the marching dunes. When, after driving out the Axis armies, the British took over, they used the concrete floor of this warehouse as a tennis court. Now there is not even the space for ping-pong.

The town is in an ambush between two winds—the winds form the south which bring the dust in from the Sahara, and the Mediterranean winds sweeping up the sands from the seashore. These two air streams meet in collision and jettison their dust into dunes, which in turn, line up like an army advancing on a massive front.

It need not be. The causes and the answers are obvious enough. The winds unchecked will keep on manoeuvring the loose sand. But the winds need not be unchecked nor the sands loose. Trees can provide windbreaks while with trees and binding grasses the moving dunes can be brought to a halt.

With their fuel-hunger, that very proper desire to keep warm and to cook their food, the nomads appear to have developed a fetish about trees, an instinct which makes them prey upon them without rhyme or reason.

When the Eighth Army drove out the Italians, the desert Arabs celebrated their liberation by cutting down or tearing up a million trees which the colonists had planted. When the UNO Assembly decision promising an independent Libya was announced the youngsters of Zuara mafficked by wrenching up the green shoots which the British in their turn had planted.

Then, again, there are these 'black locusts', the hungry

goats. With their habit of cropping every green shoot, they are the 'fifth column' of the advancing sands.

The 'caretaker' British Administration, whose writ runs in conjunction with Koranic law, could not ride roughshod, as the Fascists did, over these habits, however much they might deplore them. They had to persuade the local Arabs to introduce and enforce their own laws to deal with destruction. Here again, it was not easy, because settlers' rights and nomads' rights are often in conflict and a nomad is just as resentful about the enclosure of a piece of meaningless desert as the Council for the Preservation of Rural England would be about the impounding of our commons.

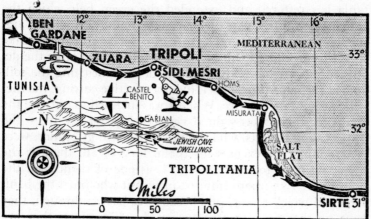

The local Arab Administration of Zuara, however, passed by-laws and made it a crime, within their jurisdiction, to destroy trees or graze animals on the sprouting defences of the dunes which had once again to be fixed. Fences were erected to bar the way of wandering tribes and divert them to less vulnerable pasture.

The Town Council of Zuara had public opinion with them in this instance. There was the visible evidence of the sand-invasion of the town to endorse the order.

It is not only in the immediate coastal region that these precautions have to be taken, for there are areas of moving dunes far inland which constantly threaten the coastal farmlands. By patient persuasion the British authorities managed to get possession of these dunes and marked them out in squares five yards by five. Round the squares they planted dess, a coarse local grass which soon begins to act as a dwarf hedge to protect the acacia-tree saplings planted in the centre. By hiring Arab rangers (on the principle of poacher turned game-keeper) they held off the nomads and their goats. The grasses self-seeded, encouraged any latent herbage which was there, and in a short time matted the sand until the dunes were as securely protected from the wind as if they had been covered by a tarpaulin.

By such methods the Agricultural Department of Tripolitania has restored and extended the green belt which the Italians began to create 25 years ago around Tripoli, enlarging the radius farther and farther into the desert. In ten years' time this green belt will be a rich forest serving alike the defensive purpose of holding off the desert, enriching the soil, and, at the same time, providing, by selective cutting, the fuel which the Arabs require. When I was inclined to criticise the Arabs for their short-sighted vendetta against the trees, the conservation experts, who should have a real grievance, were generous in their excuses for them. First of all, there is the desperate need for fuel. Secondly, as one of them said, the nomads are like troops billeted in transit who burn the banisters and wreck rooms, just because, as passers-through, they have no thought of tomorrow, or the discomforts they are creating. Thirdly, when you get on reasonable terms with the Bedouins and have the patience to indulge in those interminable arguments which they love, they are persuadable and teachable. It is a matter of wrestling with the habits of thousands of years, with *Kismet* (fate) and with that fatal phrase *Allah will provide*.

One local commissioner in Tripolitania told me how after a drought he had gone to commiserate with a Bedouin sheikh who had lost the entire crop of barley on which the year's grain for his tribe depended. All he said was 'Allah be praised'. When the surprised commissioner pressed the point, the sheikh said that he would not now have to do the threshing.

Anyway, 'Allah will provide'. Allah, through the British tax-payer, did so in the form of relief shipments.

Tripolitania, climatically, is a country of sharp contrasts. In the coastal belts the annual rainfall can average 16 inches, but 70 miles inland it drops to 8 inches and then an hour's motor drive farther on, it is down to 4 inches. One would expect a mild Mediterranean climate, but Tripolitania has had the world's highest temperature—136 degrees Fahrenheit recorded at Azizia near Tripoli, on September 13th, 1922. The map gives the explanation—the Gulf of Sirte is the deepest dent which the Mediterranean makes into Africa, a thrust towards the rich tropics. That fact of geography also explains the origin of *Tripoli,* which means 'The Three Towns'. These were the ancient Emporia—Sabratha, Oea (on the site of modern Tripoli) and Leptis Magna—which were the trading ports of the early Phoenicians because they were the termini of the shortest trade routes to the slaves, ivory and gold dust of Central Africa.

Fascist Italy set out to restore the ancient productivity of Tripolitania and to make it once again the granary of Rome. The Italians made their mistakes.

We visited ghost towns, Italian settlements abandoned long before the liberation of the Arabs threatened their security. They were founded in the belief that they would get fresh water but they ran instead into salt deposits. Yet these towns could be revived if the wells were pushed down to 1,000 feet instead of the 800 feet where they struck salt water. The salt-layer could be sealed off.

While in the great plain just behind Tripoli a green belt can be established with modern equipment, the future prosperity of the territory probably lies in olives. For the first time since the classical era, Tripoli, in 1949-50, had an export—5,000 tons—of oil. That came mainly from the great olive plantations which the Italians had planted 12 years earlier and which had just reached maturity, as well as from the age-old olive groves. We saw olive trees which have been yielding for 64 generations, for 2,000 years. How do they know? Because the descendants of 64 generations claim their share in the produce of the family tree. There are hundreds of them scattered all over the world who can produce a title to their share and to whom the authorities can be held accountable even if that share could barely dress a salad. Later in Palestine I was to find similar trees cropped under similar practice in which the shares were reckoned in 100/thousandths.

There is a noticeable contrast between the Arab olive-groves and the Italian. The Italian are in marshalled and dis-ciplined rows, like an army on parade; the Arab have the scattered abandon of English parkland. It is interesting to hear soil conservationists arguing the relative merits. In the Italian groves the cultivators plough between the serried rows; in the Arab groves they plough the tilth around the trees. One expert got positively apoplectic about some of the Italian groves and some of the Italian fields which were ploughed in beautiful straight furrows running north and south. He pointed out that the prevailing winds were north and south and would comb soil from the furrows by wind erosion.

Within the Green Belt area there is a rich harvest to be had of citrus fruits, almonds, vegetables and soft fruits. They can grow strawberries here, and export them to Covent Garden by air two months ahead of any other place; one can have fresh Tripolitania strawberries in January.

To see the real possibilities of the so-called 'desert' one has to go to Sidi Mesri, the experimental station south-east of Tripoli. They have a photograph there of what existed in 1911—a Turkish Agricultural College right out in the desert. Whoever built it must have done so as an act of faith. That faith has certainly been justified, for today it is a 180-acre botanical garden, with an endless variety of trees and plants from all climatically equivalent parts of the world. Here they are tested and adapted to the rigours of the soil and the climate. They are watered by eight wells with tall windmills to do the pumping, and one can see the miracle wrought by water. Ordinary desert sand without treatment even with fertilisers will give large crops of properly selected barley and

hundreds of tons per acre of lucerne. Here they have introduced spineless cactus from the American continent for
animal fodder. From Tunisia they have introduced 'Florence
aurore wheat' as an early-growing, disease-resistant high-
yielder, to revolutionise the grain production of Tripolitania.
They are trying out various varieties of acacia which lend
themselves to natural hedging and to windbreaks. There are
great avenues of eucalyptus trees from Australia. There is the
casuarina, also from Australia, which, with its whip-like
branches and iron-wood, can be an effective brake on the
*sirocco*, or *khamseen*.

The laboratories at Sidi Mesri are exceedingly well
equipped. By some curious dispensation they escaped damage
and pilfering by the passing armies. The instruments and the
resources of the Station, both for pure and applied research
into desert problems, are excellent. The Italians claimed that
it was the finest research establishment in Africa. It is certain
that its capacity for research is far greater than the requirements of Tripoli, or, indeed, of North Africa. There it was
impressed upon me that it ought to be turned into an international laboratory of the kind which Unesco conceived in relation to the general problem of the whole arid zone. As it is,
at the moment, it is a rather depressing white elephant. The
British caretaker administration has been able to do little else
than look after it. There is a small staff of Italian scientists
and a few British experts who are more interested in the
applied side than in pure research. Nevertheless, it renders a
useful service in dealing with immediate problems.

One of the most interesting aspects at Sidi Mesri is its work
on animal husbandry. I left convinced of the importance of
animal breeding as a contribution to the recovery and better-
ment of the desert. Sometimes people talk of agricultural
science as 'making two blades of grass grow where one grew
before'. Here science is trying to make one animal grow where
two grew before. Desert vegetation is sparse, but scraggy,
underfed animals may eat as much as profitable, well-bred
animals. If you can get more and better milk, more and better
meat, more and better work, and, as in the case of poultry,

more and better eggs and flesh, or in the case of sheep, sweeter and better mutton from the available grazing, that alone can mean a big improvement in the standard of living of people in desert areas.

We drove round the city of Tripoli in a fiacre, an open carriage driven by a villainous-looking wall-eyed Berber, who— although I am quite sure I am doing him a great injustice— looked quite capable of kidnapping me and carrying me off to the desert, except that his horse could never have got us there. It was a caricature of a horse. It might have been Rosinante, the decrepit steed on which Don Quixote went tilting at windmills. Then I remembered that Rosinante was probably a Spanish jennet, bred from the Moorish *barbs,* and the barb, or Barbary 'pony', had come from this part of Africa. They were descended from the horses which, long before Arab times, made the ancient Libyans the great horsemen who introduced the Greeks (and through them the Romans) to four-horse chariot racing. Herodotus (484 B.C.), 'Father of History', described how the Garamantes, the warrior tribe of the Fezzan, south of Tripoli, used to chase the Ethiopian cavemen in their four-horse chariots. Looking at old Rosinante between the shafts of the Tripoli cab, one pitied the degeneracy of a noble breed. That was true of most of the barbs which one could see in the coastal belt, though as I was to find later, with dramatic effect, the Bedouin barbs of the desert riders are still pretty good stock.

All the thoroughbreds in the world are descended from English racehorses, but when the British boast of their 'bloodstock' they must remember that by *blood* is meant *Arab blood* and that the Derby winners and all the other aristocrats of the racing world spring from desert animals. They all trace back in direct male line to Byerly Turk, Darley Arabian and Godolphin. Godolphin, the most famous of them all, was a barb, like this Tripoli cab-horse. Indeed, the Godolphin was discovered in Paris, in 1728, drawing a water-cart. So, when we admire the speed and grace of a racehorse, we should acknowledge the debt we owe to the desert.

The Controller of Agriculture of Tripoli, Mr. Taylor, remembered that debt and decided to try some reverse lease-lend. He wanted to cross-breed the degenerate barb with healthy, wholesome and sturdy British stock. He went back to Britain to find suitable sires for crossing with the local types for draught and remount purposes. He made an inspection of local breeds in Britain, 'settled' for Welsh cobs, and Dale and Fell ponies, and had some prize animals shipped out to Sidi Mesri. The offspring of these hardy British types would help to repay the debt we owe to the barb.

But lend-lease in breeding is not confined to barbs. The native cattle, sheep and poultry are hardy but thriftless types. It would be no good, however, merely to choose highly placed specimens from western farmyards. It would be like taking a Mayfair debutante out of the cocktail lounge and expect her to do what Arab women do—carry loads of brushwood forty miles across the desert. So any breeds put into the desert must stand up to the local conditions.

That is why Mr. Jean Etienne le Riche, the South African who is the livestock officer of the British Administration, went off to the Sudan and shipped back by aeroplane selected specimens of the Kenana breed of the *zebu,* or hump-back cattle. This ox, sometimes called the Brahman bull, has a hump of fat on the shoulders and was transplanted from India into the Sudan, where it readily adapted itself to African conditions. This breed has all the desired characteristics required by the climatic conditions of the African desert yet at the same time can improve the beef, draught and milking qualities of the native stock. In Tripoli they insist upon cattle with this triple purpose, but I was to find in Egypt and later in Iraq quite different views on what ought to be expected from desert animals.

The Barbary sheep is an ancient breed of high quality. Its yellow fleece may have been the origin of the myth of the Golden Fleece. It is a hardy desert type, with a fat tail, which is a sort of natural knapsack in which the animal hoards fat to sustain it during the hungry season. Even when for days there is no water to drink, it will get its liquid from the dew of its dawn grazing or from the desert plants which it eats, the

leaves of which are thick and succulent beneath a wax-like
coating.

Before he came into North Africa, with the South African
forces in the war, Le Riche was a farmer in South-West Africa,
where he had flocks of karakoul, soft-coated sheep, the pelt of
which is 'Persian Lamb'. The sheep, as the 'Persian Lamb' sug-
gests, came from the steppes of Asia and he conceived the idea
that, by marrying the breeds of the Western and the Asiatic
Deserts, he could make the fleece of the Barbary sheep once
again a 'golden fleece'—a new source of economic wealth for
North Africa.

Before I finished with the desert, I was to have a close
acquaintance with desert poultry. The stand-by in desert
outposts is not canned foods, but eggs—eggs no bigger than
those of plovers—and, for the inevitable *cous-cous*, scraggy
chickens. The desert fowls have to be capable of scraping a
living out of a reluctant soil. There are two native breeds in
Tripolitania, a tufted variety which the Arabs significantly
call 'The Roman Chicken' and another which seems to be a
smaller version of the game birds of Britain or India. So, from
the poultry houses of Sidi Mesri, they brought zest to the
ancient strains from the southern oases and successfully crossed
them with a type of British brown leghorn which has a strain
of Indian jungle fowl, and may have a kinship with the desert
types. The quality of the birds has been improved and so have
the output and the quality of the eggs.

There are also extensive piggeries at the research stations,
where they are experimenting with the animals in the hope
that they may be able to establish a profitable pork and bacon
industry. But the prospects of inducing the Arabs to take up
pig breeding, however profitable, are not very good. Like the
Jews, the Moslems are barred by their faith from eating pork
or from having anything to do with the abomination which is
the swine. In the past there must have been good, sound
reasons for this ban on pig-meat. Like the other injunctions
in that sanitary code, the public health by-laws, of Chapter XI
of Leviticus, the 'uncleanness' of the pigs had a relation to
the diseases fostered under climatic and desert conditions. But

WADHI IN
SPATE:
Deeply erod-
ed water
courses, in
the desert,
flood for a few
days a year.

...RAN SILT:
...his spread
... soil over
...and. The
...acks, dries
...st, and is
...n away.

DESERT VI
Women, b
of burden,
ing with
faggots f
infidel cam

—AND WI
IT CAN
This parkla
(complete v
Yorkshirem
was Liby
desolati
thirty ye
ago.

even if modern science could guarantee the pig against these, the sanction of religion and of time would make it difficult to persuade the Arabs to tend him.

There is a deeper significance to this animal breeding. These earnest and devoted people—the scientists and experts who are wrestling with the desert problems—realise that the animals which can make those deserts can also redeem the deserts and are, moreover, the common bond between the pastoral tribes and the settled farmers—between Abel and Cain.

Another interesting feature of Sidi Mesri was the ambitious but not very successful attempt by the Italians to produce a solar-engine. This solar energy plant consists of a normal coal fire boiler with a chlorifier containing ethyl-chloride. The process is to allow the sun sheet to play on the glass tubes of the chlorifier which contains the chemical in liquid form. The chemical boils at 12 degrees centigrade and forms a gas. The gas passes through a cooling cylinder and returns in liquid form to the pressure chamber to continue the circuit. The coal fire boiler goes into action by an automatic switch which operates when the sun sheet fails. As the effective working of the chlorifier is only about five hours a day, the system is not very efficient.

The Three Cities of Tripolitania originally founded by Phoenicians from Tyre about 1,000 B.C. came under the domination of Carthage before 500 B.C. Massissina, King of Numidia and enemy of Carthage, made himself the master of the Three Cities in the interval between the Second and Third Punic Wars, and when Rome finally destroyed Carthage in 146 B.C., Sabratha remained in the Numidian kingdom as an 'Allied Town' and was later annexed to the Roman province of Africa, first as a municipality and later as a colony. The city reached great prosperity in the 2nd century A.D. when the magnificent buildings which still survive as impressive ruins were built, and a thriving export trade of olive oil and African products was carried on. (*Sabratha* means 'grain market'.) In the third and fourth centuries Sabratha fell

F

on bad times, particularly from the ravages of the Vandals, but when the Byzantine Emperor, Justinian, the great law maker, reconquered North Africa, Sabratha had a revival for about a century, the era of the construction of the Christian churches. Finally, in the 7th century, the city was abandoned to the Arab conquerors. The Arabs were not town dwellers and only the central city of Oea was maintained as a fortress.

The same story is true of Leptis, except that it acquired even greater glory because one of its local boys 'made good', and became the Emperor Septimius Severus (A.D. 191-211). This was the Emperor who died at York. In his day, Leptis had a population of 80,000, which is about that of York today.

After the Arab invasion came the sand invasions, and the ruins were buried to re-emerge in our day because Mussolini spent vast amounts of money in excavating them and restoring them as probably the finest surviving example of Roman provincial cities anywhere—including Italy itself. They are not entirely unscathed because they were located by archaeologists at the end of the 17th century, when the French Consul sent statues and 600 marble columns from Leptis to Louis XIV, and later George IV 'borrowed' the columns for the construction of the sham ruins which exist by the lake at Virginia Water.

At Sabratha, the Italians practically restored to its original appearance the magnificent theatre dating from A.D. 180 and the largest in Africa, accommodating 5,000 people. One of its remarkable features is a fresco round the 'footlights' of the stage which 'bills' in permanent carvings the various attractions of the theatre—drama, comedy, ballet, orchestral concerts and choirs.

One can walk again the market-place and see the booths, with their solid stone counters, or visit the Roman, Greek and Egyptian temples, or the Christian basilicas. In Leptis there are magnificent public baths, the social centre of the city, used equally by men and women. These baths were started by the Emperor Hadrian, who could divide his attention between mixed bathing in Leptis Magna and building a wall to separate Scotland and England.

In the baths was the central saloon, which had a vaulted roof rising above the rest of the building where people met and gossiped before taking advantage of the *frigidaria,* the cold baths; the *tepidaria,* the warm baths; the *calidaria,* the hot baths; and the *laconica,* the 'turkish' baths. The latter can be recognised by the raised floors and the ducts in the wall, which admitted the hot air from the furnaces underneath.

These public baths and the innumerable private baths in the villas indicate a considerable water supply. The storage arrangements, rain cisterns in every house and building, show that they husbanded their water carefully in the cities themselves, but the main supplies came from the Jebel by aqueducts, which were 70 to 100 miles long. Recently, as Professor G. Caputo, the Italian archaeologist who supervises the ruins and the restoration work which still goes on under the British Administration, pointed out to me, a remarkable discovery was made. In the Jebel there were great olive groves and I went to see the Roman olive presses there. The ancient Romans, knowing that oil and water do not mix, used the ingenious device of pouring the oil on the surface of the water and using the aqueducts as a free-flowing method of transporting it to the coast. How they skimmed off the oil, I did not discover, but it would not have been difficult.

The tour of the Jebel was an exciting and rather alarming excursion, because the coastal edge of the mountains is precipitous and ascending it by car makes one feel like a fly walking up a window-pane. Any alarm was imaginary rather than real, however, because the military road which the Italians built is a solid and remarkable engineering feat. There must be hundreds of hair-pin bends.

All the way up those precipitous slopes, there is a system of terraces, glorified window-boxes, laboriously constructed with boulders and borrowed soil by the Berbers, who, as distinct from the desert nomads, are careful and thrifty cultivators. On the summit of the ridge which we climbed was an old Berber town, and it was market day.

In the square was a jostling mass of Berbers and hordes of children, and in the middle of all the swarthy youngsters was a curly redhead with a freckled face—a four-year-old on a donkey who was holding his own in a mixture of Italian and Arabic. On closer acquaintance he turned out to be the son of the local Commissioner. Until seven months before he had never been out of Glasgow, from which his father and mother came. He was the only non-African child for 100 miles. In that short time he had picked up enough Italian (which the Berbers acquired during the long Italian occupation) and Arabic to act as his mother's interpreter in the kitchen and, if necessary, to provide his father with the right expletives. When I last saw him he was being carried pick-aback over the mountains by a Berber.

The Jebel has great possibilities for olive and vine growing, and the Berbers are only too anxious to co-operate.

These mountains were the haunts of the Long Range Desert Group, those remarkable adventurers who, during the war, roamed the desert behind the Italian and German lines collecting intelligence and conducting sudden raids which disrupted the enemy's lines of communication and demoralised their troops. Here were dropped, at critical moments in the war, Arab-speaking parachutists who, protected by friendly Arabs, donned desert robes and lived in the nomad encampments. When we visited the troglodyte cave settlements in the depths of the Jebel, we were warmly received by a sheikh who wore on his *gandoura* the ribbon of the Order of the British Empire, which he was awarded for his part in assisting these paratroopers.

This visit to the caves was not a social call. We were trying to find the Jewish troglodytes, who for at least 800 years had lived underground in these mountains. Even their synagogue was a cave and throughout the centuries they had lived practically unmolested and on close and friendly terms with the Moslems. Now, however, their caves were empty. The missionaries from Israel had arrived ahead of us to claim them as one of the Lost Tribes and to win them back to Palestine. Only a few weeks before, the modern Exodus had taken place and the entire community, with all their goods and chattels, had set off for the Holy Land.

The Arabs had always lived in hut-dwellings in the villages adjoining the Jewish cave dwellings and when the Jews had gone, the caves had been left abandoned or used to stable animals. In a few months, caves which had been occupied for centuries (one definitely for 750 years) had begun to collapse, showing the care which had been practised in maintaining the caves intact. Then the Arabs had discovered the amenities of cave dwelling, and we saw new caves being dug. The workmen were of a special tribe from the Fezzan, where, according to Herodotus, the Negro troglodytes lived 2,500 years ago. They had been brought hundreds of miles to practise their traditional craft as domestic 'sappers'. One can have a commodious pit-cave for £40. It is quite wrong to regard these cave-dwellings as something primitive, or cave-mannish, because in fact they are a highly civilised form of living. Indeed, one of the Italian Governors had a special cave constructed, not as a deep shelter but as a summer cottage. The caves are cool in the heat and warm in the chilly nights. There is everything to commend cave-dwelling as a form of desert living.

All over the Jebel and far into the deserts beyond are the Roman systems of water conservation—catchment dams, or diversion dams, on the *wadhis,* underground reservoirs in the hills, and wells. It is estimated that there are thousands of Roman wells and cisterns in Tripolitania. Over 200 have been discovered and over 100 have been cleaned out and are functioning just as efficiently as they did 2,000 years ago. They had been choked up with drifting sand, and, in at least one instance, with piled-up skeletons from some tribal affray perhaps centuries ago. The British authorities rebuild the well-heads and fit them with means of haulage. Sometimes the desert tribes prefer to let their women do the hauling of the water. Sometimes they tether camels or donkeys to the rope which hauls up the buckets. The new wellheads are equipped with concrete troughs so that the herd and the camels do not have to be hand-watered. If these wells were equipped with pumps they could become not just drinking holes but oases—irrigated plots.

One of the best services that could be rendered to Tripolitania would be to recruit squads of junior archaeologists and geologists to go out and explore the deserts in search of such water-traps. Finding these wells and cisterns would not be re-creating history, like the discovery of the tombs of kings, but it would be creating new history, because it would be helping to feed people of our own generation.

Descending from the Jebel we drove eastwards along the coastal road. Along that road streaked the Eighth Army chasing the retreating forces of Rommel. The retreat was so fast that, although there were treacherous mines and booby traps, there was no serious engagement except at Homs, which is the modern counterpart of Leptis Magna. Here the Germans fought a rearguard action with the 51st Division, when the Highlanders had a bitter fight for 'Edinburgh Castle', the nickname of the Turkish fort on the heights. The silhouette of that castle and the rock on which it stands readily suggested that name.

On the journey, Le Riche pointed out to me a peculiarity of the desert which I had not noticed before. Wherever a tree or a shrub had checked the drifting sands, there was herbage on the windward side of the pile. This vegetation was another proof of the curious fertility for which we rarely give the desert credit. That soil had come from the far-distant Sahara in the duststorms sweeping up from the south.

The heavier, rough grains of sand had been shed at various stages of the journey and finally in the crossing of the Jebel, only the finest dust of all had carried on until it came into collision with the Mediterranean winds and had dropped here a rich *loess* or powdered loam. It is so fine that it is difficult to imagine that these particles carry their original nourishment and fertility with them. But there it is, and the wind-blown soil and the wind-blown seeds come together per-sistently to produce desert vegetation.

At Sirte, I was supposed to be handed over, formally, by the Tripolitanian Administration to the Administration of

Cyrenaica. The transportation from Benghazi, however, had not arrived and there was nothing to do but to wait.

The local Arab Commissioner installed me in a small desert rest-house. The only means of communication was by radio signal from a police post at 8 o'clock each morning, and one could expect a reply at 8 o'clock next morning. The rest-house was a two-roomed bungalow with camp beds and one ate at a *bistro* overlooking what was once a major Italian airfield. It has now returned to desert.

During that enforced wait I learned something of the fatalism that grows upon one in the desert. Time stands still. All those carefully planned appointments, air-take-offs and newspaper deadlines cease to have any reality. The only thing which is real is the Technicolored pageantry of the desert.

That pageantry on the first day became a memorable event. There was a great thudding of horses and the rest-house was suddenly surrounded by a cohort of Bedouin horsemen with their flowing robes and muffling headgear, who had appeared out of the Nowhere. For one brief spasm (with memories of desert 'thrillers') I thought they had come to carry me off and hold me to ransom. I flattered myself. This was a great cere-monial display and the occasion had nothing to do with me. One of the great Arab leaders, Bischir Sidawi Bey, had been the spokesman of Libyan independence at Lake Success and was returning from Benghazi accompanied by the Grand Mufti of Tripolitania. As the rest-house was the only thing which resembled a hotel, they were to share close quarters with me for the night. News of their approach had spread through the desert. Here, where with the resources of modern science I could not get an answer for 48 hours, news travels fleet-foot to the distant tribal encampments. They formed a mounted escort before their leader on the outskirts of Sirte and led him in triumph to the guest-house. Then they demon-strated. Their barbs reared and cavorted in their colourful saddle blankets and silver-encrusted trappings.

The sheikhs, according to their wealth and importance, wore silver and gold bindings to their headgear. They were muffled in white and presently they started chanting their hymn of courageous manhood and heroic death, punctuated by cries and waving of strong right arms, in a gesture which only needed rifles to complete it. The excited camels started trumpeting, the donkeys, not to be outdone, began braying, and unseen women concealed somewhere started uttering shrill, bird-like calls. Everyone and everything became excited.

Presently, on a signal from one of the sheikhs, they, with one accord, wheeled their horses and a hundred strong raced down the road. They had suddenly decided to improvise a horse race and on the one-time airfield lined up. It was not a race, it was a charge, sheikhs goading their horses into a thundering gallop with the ugly, sharp pointed heels of their silver stirrups. Then the swirling mob at the winning post sorted itself out, and the riders cantered back again and grouped themselves around young passionate men in smartly tailored suits and red *tarbushes* who harangued them with violent oratory, punctuated by choruses of 'Libya, Libya'.

That night Sidawi Bey and the Grand Mufti insisted that hospitality, which is an injunction of the Prophet, demanded that they play host to me, a stranger in their country. As we assailed a monster *cous-cous*, which severely taxed my waistband and my politeness, the statesman and the religious leader of Tripolitania discussed with me fluid mechanics and hydrology!

Three motor-cars in succession had set out from Benghazi to try to reach me. All three had broken down on the hazardous desert roads. On the sixth day I 'hitch-hiked' in a car which was returning from Tripoli to Benghazi.

# CHAPTER SIX

## ON THE TRAIL OF THE DESERT RATS

WE started at dawn. Overnight there had been a shower of rain. As the sun rose above the horizon I experienced the still ecstasy of the desert. The whole landscape was suffused in a green blush as delicate as a maiden's modesty—the sudden growth of plants in response to the rain gives, not so much a cover, as a complexion to the sands of the desert. As the day advanced we saw the miracle of the desert flowers in vivid contrast to the lichenous grey of the persistent bushes and shrubs with which I had grown familiar throughout the journey. There were square miles of flaming reds, triumphant yellows and strident blues. It was no longer the coy greenery of the dawn. This was the fickle desert, dressed up like Carmen Miranda in Technicolored sashes.

As we approached the Cyrenaican frontier, the evidence of the past battles advanced to meet us. We had to make wide detours across the *wadhis* because of blown bridges and bomb craters. Nor was it safe to make too wide a detour, because large stretches of this area are still heavily mined.

For miles before we reached "Marble Arch" we were travelling through a graveyard of war equipment. The human metal-carrions have been busy and the tanks, cars, lorries and aeroplanes have been picked to the bare skeletons of everything easily movable. The whole landscape was a junk-heap with oil drums and petrol tins. There were no American jerricans. These substantial containers, now the saddle-gourds —the water-bottles on the camels—of the nomads, were rather comically poised on the heads of the water-women. For some reason or other, however, the ordinary tins and drums had been despised by the metal scavengers. It was then that I divided the desert regions into yet another character—the *hammada*, or dry stony plateau; the *erg*, the region of the sand dunes; and now the *tin-can*, the desert of rusting metal.

Then on the horizon, out of nothingness, 'Marble Arch' appeared. I suppose I had expected a broad triumphal arch. Instead this looked like the head of a needle, with the dead straight road threaded through it and emptiness all round. Then, through this needle's eye, came a train of camels, after which I was prepared to believe anything in the desert.

'Marble Arch' must have been doodled by Mussolini absent-mindedly on his blotting pad. It is a monumental piece of bombast, which cannot make up its mind whether to be an arch or a pagoda. It marks the legendary boundary of Greece and Carthage—'legendary' because it stands beside the mounds of the Philainoi, the 'fame seekers'.

According to the story the Carthaginians and the Greeks of Cyrene had got bored with the continuous war over a non-existent frontier and decided to settle it by a trial of strength —Africans would be sent as envoys and wherever they met in the desert, that would be the frontier.

The Greeks were delayed for some reason and had only got a third of the distance when they met the two Carthaginian brothers, Philainoi. They accused the brothers of cheating, and to 'call their bluff' suggested that the Cartha-ginians should either agree to being buried alive on the spot in proof of their claim or allow the Greeks to advance their claim on the same conditions — to be buried alive as a frontier post. The Philainoi accepted the challenge and were

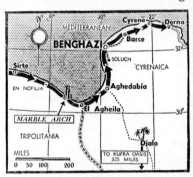

entombed at 'Marble Arch'. Their graves became the bor-der between Greece and Carthage and, in modern times, between Tripolitania and Cyrenaica.

The pointers were beginning to say 'El Agheila'. El Agheila! A major objective in the desert war. With what mixed feelings people read that recurring name in the head-lines! 'Jumbo' Wilson went through to El Agheila in Wavell's campaign—and went back. Neil Ritchie went through in Auchinleck's campaign—and went back. Montgomery went through in Alexander's campaign—and did not go back. What an important place it seemed to us all! And how insignificant it is in fact. One might easily pass it unnoticed. It consists of a low dune-fort, with parapets no higher than a suburban garden wall, a mosque, a warehouse, two clay huts and two shops made out of scrap iron. One of these shacks calls itself a 'restaurant', but its stock consisted of a sand-encrusted German magneto, the bonnet of an Italian car, three bars of Naafi chocolate (1942 issue), four cakes of desert-chafed British soap, two cans of American food, a biscuit tin of carob beans, a box of sugar and a cask of green tea. There was no food and I ordered a cup of Turkish coffee, made with water out of a petrol can and served in a whisky glass. I drank it sitting in the pilot's seat from a wrecked German Stuka.

The Arab storekeeper would not accept money for the coffee (but charged five shillings for the eight-year-old chocolate). He insisted I was his guest. We went through the 'ritual of the tea', which had now become familiar to me. A charcoal brazier, about the size of a soup can, for which he provided the draught by a wicker Japanese fan, was his stove. With a tiny teapot, in which he put green tea and lots of sugar, he boiled the tea, poured it into a small glass, sipped it, (disapprovingly), poured it back into the teapot and added a handful more tea, repeating this unhygienic but hospitable rite four times before he, with salaams, handed me the glass. By the time we had reached a third glass, which is socially obligatory, I reckoned that the tea was one-third spittle, one-third sugar and one-third mint.

On the 230-mile journey from the frontier to Benghazi there was virtually no cultivation whatever. It was the land of the nomads, whose wanderings were made perilous by the booby traps and mines. We could hear explosions. The battlefield of eight years before was still claiming its casualties. Many of the places which loomed large on the war-time maps are so insignificant that I could not even identify them until we got to Aghedabia. It is a considerable town heavily devastated by the battle but which I recall mainly as the place where I watched Arab schoolboys playing football while a burst tyre was being repaired, and as an oasis in the *tin-can* desert. Here at least they found a use for the tin cans. They filled them with moist clay and used them as building blocks for their mud huts. A thin metal will rust away, but by then the clay will have hardened into solid bricks.

Twenty miles out of Benghazi, olive groves and tilled fields begin to appear. The approaches to the city are through avenues of trees—eucalyptus.

Benghazi is the capital of Cyrenaica, a country more than three times the size of Great Britain. While Britain has to accommodate 50,000,000 people in its 95,000 square miles, Cyrenaica, with an area of 330,000 square miles, has less than one person per square mile. Most of the area is desert and practically the entire population are nomads. This is the land of the Senussi, a strict Mohammedan fraternity. Sidi Muhammad el Senussi (1796-1859), who traced his descent from Fatima, the daughter of the Prophet, founded the first *zawiya*, or college, of the sect in 1835. The Senussi are a puritanical Islamic sect but they are also a warrior tribe of desert nomads and a powerful political force. They formed a continual resistance to the Italian occupation of Libya and Marshal Graziani, who was sent out to pacify them, took violent measures against them and set out to exterminate their leaders, compelling the Grand Senussi to flee into exile. During the war, the Senussi joined forces with the British and, by the alliance, got an undertaking that Cyrenaica would become an independent State. In 1949, the British honoured this undertaking by granting Cyrenaica a constitution, with the Grand Senussi established as Emir. Under the United Nations' decision, Cyrenaica and Tripolitania will become 'United Libya' in 1952.

The name 'Cyrenaica' derives from Cyrene, the great colony of the ancient Greeks, and today, one of the most interesting ruined cities in the world. Cyrene was founded in the 7th century B.C. According to Herodotus it was begun by Battus, of the Greek island of Thera (now Santorin), who went to consult the Delphic Oracle about his stammer and was told that the only cure was to found a settlement in Libya. Since he was rather vague as to where Libya was, he and his followers made two false attempts on islands which they mistook for Libya. He still stammered and when he reproached the Oracle, he was scolded in terms which in modern jargon would run something like this: 'Wise guy, huh. You who have never been to Libya and seen it abounding with cattle and fleeces, think that you can fool me who have been there'. So Battus went further afield and successfully founded Cyrene 'at the place where the sky leaks'. According to the same historian, Ancient Cyrenaica could count on three harvests a year. To-day Barce, the high plains which constitute the bulge in the coastline of Cyrenaica, is still a potentially fruitful place, with a rainfall of up to thirty inches a year. On the Barce Plain, where nearly a thousand years before Christ the Libyans had bred fleet horses, the British Administration have, by mechanised methods, developed great prairie tracts of wheat. With no artificial or other fertilisers, substantial crops of excellent hard wheat have been harvested.

Recent surveys have shown that the whole Cyrenaican Jebel could be converted into olive plantations 100 miles long and 25 miles wide on 1,500,000 acres of valuable soil. Olives are native to this area and occur wild. Other crops which have stood the test of time are carobs, grapes and barley. A camel census has accounted for 83,000 animals and the sheep population is 410,000, with almost as many goats.

The experts hold that by decreasing the goats the sheep flocks would be increased to 2,000,000. The development even of historically fertile parts of Cyrenaica from Tobruk to Benghazi, excluding the extensive areas like the famous one at Kufi, will depend entirely on modern methods and mechanisation. The proposals are for great co-operative farm schemes, with proper mechanical equipment, and co-operative purchasing and marketing arrangements. This means persuading a desert population which is traditionally nomadic and tribal to settle down.

While next door in Egypt a population of 22,000,000 is bursting the seams of the Nile Valley to which it is confined, in Cyrenaica the problem is not too many people on the land but too few. The 330,000 Cyrenaicans are not sufficient to maintain in proper cultivation without large-scale modern methods even the existing cultivated land, far less to push out and reclaim the desert.

It was the deliberate policy of the Italian Fascists to drive the native population out into the desert to make room for the colonial settlements now abandoned, and to deny to the Arabs any access to education. Only now are secondary schools (two —at Derna and Benghazi) being established. There is no resemblance to a university or technical colleges. The result is that there are no qualified Cyrenaican experts for research, or even for land management. Even in five years' time there will be only a trickle from the secondary schools where the tribesmen can board their children.

As one intelligent Cyrenaican put it to me: 'If we have to rely on our own resources, the first Chief Justice of an independent Cyrenaica will be a youth of 21'. And when asked who that would be, he said: 'I do not know. He has only just started school'.

Here is a situation in which a country has achieved an independence dearly sought, but cannot for a long time benefit by that independence unless it makes itself dependent on outside economic help and outside experts. The Italians, for imperial and military reasons, contributed, from Rome, four-fifths of the annual budget of Libya. Britain, in its capacity as caretaker, has had, annually, to provide one-fifth of the money required to keep Cyrenaica going.

I did a flight over Cyrenaica. The Barce was like a green carpet, but beyond was a desert—nothing, not even a horizon, because it was blurred between earth and sky. The desert road looked like a straight-driven plough furrow and the camel tracks like snail smears. It might have been a landscape of the moon, or the pictures you see in medical books showing particularly noxious diseases, boils, scabies, ulcers. Now and again there might be a furtive brown plot of Arab cultivation. Yet all over there were 'warts', the humps of desert trees and vegetation, so that however grim it was not completely hopeless.

This was the battlefield over which the Eighth Army advanced and retreated, advanced and retreated, and finally advanced. History was made in this desolation. Yet, if you talk to men of the Eighth Army who suffered the dust and the heat, the trials and the tribulations, they have a 'home-sickness' still for the desert. One can understand it. Even deserts as forbidding as the Western and Libyan Deserts 'get you'.

Past Derna and beyond Tobruk the contours of the desert change and go on changing. There is the great sandbelt, where the wind piles up the sand and makes it ripple like the waves of the sea, or coils it freakishly into ridges like the whorls of a finger-print, or more ambitiously into great cliffs, curved on the windward side, sheer on the face.

Our aircraft flew low over the battlefields of El Alamein into Egypt. Here Rommel's advance was stopped sixty miles from Alexandria. Here was launched one of the decisive battles of the war, and indeed of history. What a place! There it lay below us like a relief map. We could see it all, from the Mediterranean to the Qattara Depression, 30 miles to the south.

All, that is, except El Alamein, which is, as it always was, just a halt on the railway, so insignificant that we could not spot it from the air, and before the first battle it never appeared on any conventional map. We flew over the Ruweisat Ridge and Alam El Halfa Ridge, both of them natural fortresses, and, with the Qattara Depression, part of the bottleneck in which the Axis troops became stuck and which saved Egypt, the Suez Canal and the Middle East.

It was, however, the Qattara Depression which was the most impressive—or depressing. Here the bottom seemed to fall out of the desert and a great hollow half the size of Wales dropped below sea level. It looked like the nethermost pit of Dante's Inferno and one did not need to be a military specialist to understand why Rommel could not turn the line of the British defence system at El Alamein by veering south across the Depression—although the British Long Range Desert Group used tracks across it. The Qattara Depression was, according to the Axis commentators, equal to 20 military divisions. While its northern tip is 30 miles from the Mediterranean, its eastern end is about the same distance from the Nile. It is 200 miles long and 100 miles wide.

The northern escarpment of the Depression, over which we were flying, drops from 700 feet above sea level to 500 feet below sea level. In the sump below us was the white scum of the salt marsh, or *savakha*.

This salt marsh is like the *Chott Ech Chergui*, only it is below sea level instead of above. Its water cannot be explained by the local rainfall, because that does not exceed one inch per annum, nor geologically can it be the product of seepage from the Mediterranean, nor can it be a left-over from some previous age, because the Mediterranean has never had access to Qattara. To look at it one might think it was the bottom of some forgotten sea, but it is wind, not water, which has been responsible for the Depression. The wind has scoured, in fairly recent geological times, the limestone layers and scooped out this hollow. The fact that the salt marsh gives off more steam than can be explained by the surface water is due to seepage from a subterranean reservoir which underlies most of the Libyan Desert and supplies with fresh water the great oases including Siwa, 40 miles to the west. This underground lake is fed from the mountains of the south. Before reaching the Depression, however, this water passes through salty rocks.

It seems inconceivable that the Qattara Depression could ever lend itself to human settlement. It is impassable and bars all communications, but that narrow neck of 30 miles between the Mediterranean and the Depression, which the soldiers found so useful, has always been a temptation to water engineers. There has been a series of inquiries into the possibility of cutting canals and conduits through the neck of land to let the Mediterranean flow inland. This would produce a waterfall exploiting the drop between sea level and the salt marsh (the opposite effect from that at *Chott Ech Chergui* described in Chapter III.) This waterfall generating electricity would give power desperately needed, not only for the Delta industries, but also to pump water to supply the desert needs. There is the serious question, however, that since the underground water can leak upwards into the marsh, the Mediterranean brine might soak down into the underground lake and make its presence felt in the distant oases which depend on the underground supplies.

In another half-hour, on this flying geography lesson, we were over the Nile. Even the most bored and unimpressionable air traveller leans forward in his seat at the first glimpse of the Nile.

It needed modern air travel to make it possible to realise at a glance what Herodotus meant 2,500 years ago, when he spoke of Egypt being the 'Gift of the Nile'. Over Cairo, 100 miles from the sea, one looks down on the scarf of the Nile Valley stretching away to the south, the three-striped scarf, with the sheen of the river as the middle band and the narrow green banks on either side. To the north the river fans out into its delta, a patchwork formed by the branches of the river seamed by the elaborate system of irrigation and drainage canals and diced with a chess-board pattern of the fields. On either side stretches the tawny menace of the desert—the Libyan Desert to the west, the Arabian Desert to the east.

Egypt *is* the Valley of the Nile. Apart from the oases, the whole productivity of Egypt is clamped between the steep cliffs of the river bed for over 700 miles.

Egypt on the map is a country four times the size of the

G

British Isles, but its area of cultivation, confined to the limits of the Nile Valley, is less than the area of Denmark which has a sixth of the population. All the water on which the fertility of Egypt and the livelihood of its 22,000,000 people, depend, is *imported*. Not a single tributary flows into the Nile within the boundaries of Egypt. The Nile is fed by the White Nile, which has its source in Victoria Nyanza in Uganda, and by the Blue Nile, the source of which is in Lake Tana in Abyssinia.

Egypt has some of the richest soil on earth, yet the great mass of its people lives in extreme poverty. Here, if anywhere, one can see the bad effects of over-population. Something must be done to release Egypt's swarming millions from the confines of the Nile Valley, and the only answer is—the Desert.

There is water enough in the Nile to bring fertility to thousands of square miles of the desert. The desert, however, is a high plateau. To supply it with Nile water would mean pumping. Pumping means energy. Energy means expense. And irrigation water which is a continuing expense is useless.

There are great schemes for maintaining and ensuring the flow of the Nile. There is the 'Century Plan' upon which the British and the Egyptians have agreed as a means of guaranteeing for the next hundred years at least an adequate flow and an increased flow—water sufficient to bring into cultivation possibly 2,000,000 acres of Egypt. This involves the building of a barrage and a hydro-electric plant at Owens Falls in Uganda, which will provide hydro-electric power for that country, but will also control the flood waters of the Nile. A long canal is to be cut through the swamps of the Sudd, the marshy jungle of the Sudan where the Nile waters spread and waste themselves. The canal will link the deep channel of the river, prevent the dissipation of the water, and in the process recover about 2,000,000 acres of the Sudan for farming. The other part of the plan involves Abyssinia, and the creation of a barrage on Lake Tana. As one eminent Egyptian, however, said to me, the scheme makes Egypt more than ever a hostage to countries outside its borders. That is one way of

looking at it, but conversely it shows the value of international co-operation and the interdependence of countries
one upon the other.

The Egyptians are very much alive to the need for developing the desert. On the outskirts of Cairo is Heliopolis, and
there the Government has built a great Desert Institute. It is
certainly an impressive building and with the proper
resources should be one of the greatest centres of the world
for tackling the problems of the Arid Zone.

One of Egypt's 'men against the desert' is Dr. Yusef Milad
Bey, the Director of Desert Horticulture, with whom I went
off on an expedition which was to take me into the deserts of
El Alamein which I had crossed by air. We left Cairo by that
desert road through which thousands of men and thousands of
war vehicles travelled. That desert, unlike the *tin-can* desert
of Cyrenaica, has been thoroughly scavengered.

The only material which remains are the oil drums which
painted white and filled with sand now act as the guide posts
for motorists crossing the desert at night. Half-way to Alexandria, there was a sign post, pointing to 'Natruh'. The scene
was familiar but I could not think why until Milad Bey
pointed out that *natruh* means *sodium*, or salt. *Natrium* is
what appears in the table of elements as 'Na'. The dictionary
will tell you that it is Latin in origin, but Milad Bey
explained that like many more of the names of the elements
and other scientific terms, it is a legacy of the ancient Arabs.

Natruh is the *wadhi* where Egypt has its main salt manu-
facturers. It is, however, famous for something else. It is
probably the site of the original Christian monasteries. Here
still remain large Coptic monasteries which go back to the
beginning of the Christian era. The Copts are the native
Christians of Egypt and of Ethiopia. The head of the Coptic
Church is the Patriarch of Alexandria, who is also the head
of the Abyssinian Church. He is regarded as the successor of
St. Mark, who, according to the Copts, first introduced Christianity into Africa.

While the western monastic system dates from the time of
St. Benedict (about 480-544) Christian monasticism existed in

Egypt about 250 years before that. St. Anthony, who is regarded as the founder of Christian monastic institutions, gave up all his property and retired into the desert, where, followed by his disciples, he formed the first community. He died at the age of 105.

Within sight of Alexandria we turned westwards along the coast on the road to El Alamein. We passed Arab encampments and Milad Bey pointed out something significant—that in the middle of Bedouin tents they were beginning to build huts. The nomads were beginning to settle. The secret lies in the olive and fig trees, which have been introduced by the authorities and presented to the Arabs. It is a persuasive device for making the Arabs stop wandering. By age-old habits, the Bedouin of that area, as in the rest of the desert, would plough, or rather scratch up, a bit of land, sow his barley, wander off into the desert and return to harvest the crop. But give him a tree and impress upon him that it is his and must not be cut down, and he will jealously guard that tree and its fruits; and while he is sitting waiting for his fruit to grow, he will—as he is doing in this area—begin to till the ground round it. Gradually he becomes a fixture, a tiller rather than a wanderer.

Burg El Arab in the critical days of the desert campaign was the rear H.Q. On the spit of a lagoon by the sea, Montgomery set up his caravans. The Desert Air Force operated from this locality. Today it is the site of a desert research station—and a most surprising one, as I found.

In the middle of the desert was a magnificent country house, newly built, of stone, as spacious and as comfortable as a *de luxe* hotel. It had every modern luxury and convenience, and might seem, unless one understood its purpose, singularly out of place as the 'rest house' of a desert laboratory. Dr. Milad Bey explained how it had happened.

Before the war there had existed here and at Mersa Matruh two experimental plots for desert cultivation. But when the armies and the battles swept through, both were trampled back into desert. The prospects were completely discouraging. Years of work had been lost and the desert seemed even less inviting than before. Then Dr. Milad Bey, and those who supported him, decided that before the desert could be made attractive for plants, it would have to be made attractive for people. Something must be done to coax, first of all money and then staff, to come out here into the desolation. So before he even attempted to create his laboratory or restore his experimental acres, he decided to try an astute form of 'salesmanship'.

Instead of pitching tents in the wilderness, he persuaded the Government to build a magnificent hotel. There he was able to entertain the highest in the land—those who would find the money, if they wanted to, for his practical schemes. He made them 'desert-conscious' under the most congenial conditions. His weekend guests also included university professors and scientists from Cairo and Alexandria, on whom he would have to depend to find his staff.

Around it he laid out a beautiful botanical garden, which, while adding to the amenities of the rest-house, also provided the testing-ground for the trees and plants which he was trying to adapt to the desert. 'There', he could say to his guests, 'is how we can make the desert bloom'.

The device succeeded far more quickly than all the official memoranda, research prospectuses and persuasive balance sheets, which he could have presented. Ministers and others, who came and saw, were conquered. And so were 1,200 acres of desert.

The annual rainfall of this area, on a ten years' average, is about six inches. There are wells in the area but they contain a certain amount of salt which is unhealthy for the soil but which can be useful when diluted with rainwater. To get the water supply, the scientists have employed the devices of the ancient Romans. They have taken advantage of the low surrounding hills, which have been bared to the rock and act as a run-off. One acre of watershed properly harnessed can, even with this rainfall, irrigate eight acres of soil.

With the available water, 1,200 acres of desert have been reclaimed as fields for the experimental station. They have produced extensive orchards of olives, almonds, figs, peaches

and vines. There one saw endless varieties of desert plants
from all over the world. One can even see pine trees, strangely
dusty and out of place in the desert sands, but flourishing.
They nearly failed until the botanists inoculated them with
fungus of the *mycorrhiza* family, which growing on the roots
somehow extracted from the soil the nourishment which the
pines were lacking.

The modern amenities of Burg El Arab extend from the
important visitors to the farm animals. The hen-houses and
cattle sheds looked like suburban villas. There one found an
endless variety of poultry, including 25lb. turkeys. The most
successful turkey is a cross between American and Egyptian
varieties which have proved ideal under desert conditions.
A sheep-cross between the British Sussex and a native Egyptian type has appealed to the Arabs, and a cattle-cross between
a Jersey and the Damietta, the miniature type to which I have
previously referred, gives 12 litres of milk a day.

To appreciate fully, however, the practical value of this
elegant desert station, one has to leave the experimental acres
and see the service which it has done to the nomads, in settled
cultivation which extends westwards towards El Alamein.
The station attracts not only city visitors but curious tribesmen who, while they may be only impressed and mystified by
the research laboratories, can find a direct personal interest
in the demonstration fields and olive groves, and in the handi-
craft school which has been established at the station to
encourage old and nearly forgotten skills among the Arabs.

It was a revelation to see an Arab sheikh in flowing robes
and turban, with a walking stick, going round his plot like
any British farmer fingering the soil which was once the dust
his camel pads spurned and 'bawling out' his tribesmen because of faulty pruning, and to hear him boasting of his crop.

On one and a half acres a local sheikh had such a successful
year with his olives that he got 1,600 kilos of oil, worth about
£400. This was from trees planted on his tribal land since the
war by the scientists. The trees and the help of the scientists
are free as part of the settlement policy encouraged by the
Government.

With Milad Bey I drove out to what had been the underground battle headquarters during the El Alamein campaign.
The desert was perfect camouflage and without a guide it
would have been impossible to have found it.

'Mind the scorpions' cautioned Milad Bey, as we accustomed our eyes to the darkness of the shelter, after the glare
of the desert sun. These baleful creatures, with their powerful
pincers and poisonous sting, had discovered the cool comforts
of the abandoned H.Q. and were lurking in the recesses. This
was a spacious shelter of 12 rooms, including a big War Room,
where the operations were once planned. It was a magnificent
piece of engineering and a credit to the sappers of the Royal
Engineers and to modern concrete.

A mile or so across the desert, but separated by nearly 2,000
years, is another underground shelter, designed, not against
bombs, but as a water cistern by the Romans. When Dr.
Milad Bey had suggested a visit to the cistern, I had expected
something much less ambitious than this, something less than
a great underground cavern with vaulted halls and branch-
ing galleries. The main chambers were nearly 80 feet high,
and, as I stepped off the bottom stair, I nearly discovered the
depth of the water but was rescued in time. It was one of the
finest examples of Roman ingenuity in cistern construction
which I was to find on my journey. Into it, from every direction, led the runlets collecting the water from the surrounding hills. The incoming water ran over a shallow weir where
it deposited its silt before it dropped into the reservoir itself.
This capacious cistern can conserve water for years, and
there are hundreds of Roman cisterns in the Egyptian
desert.

Since it was restored nomads come ten miles or more to
draw their water ration. The mouth of the well is kept locked
against water-poachers. The supplies are pulled up by donkey-
drag. As can be well imagined, the water stored in this way,
not just for months but even for years, is not very fresh. It is,
however, very *lively*. In fact, it is teeming with life. Nothing
would have induced me to drink it after I had seen the
pink tadpoles and the scum of red organisms which swarm on

the surface, like a living rust. They do not, however, worry the nomads; they just strain them off through muslin.

Burg El Arab itself is the 'capital' of the Frontier Province, a seat of government for the desert area which extends west from the Delta to the borders of Cyrenaica, and here I met one of the traditional 'men against the desert', a British officer who, in the days of the British protectorate, was the Governor of this Province, and who like many other Britons became so infatuated with the desert that he could not leave it.

Major Wilfred Jennings-Bramley is known to the Bedouins of the Western Desert as 'Ramley Bey'. He invited us to his house. This is a fortress which he designed himself on the traditional Arab model and had it built of stone transported thirty miles across the desert from Alexandria. He received us at the massive gate, a charming little man, remarkably spry for his 79 years and weathered brown by the sixty years he has spent in the desert.

His first job was the not very exciting one of secretary to the Director-General of Customs. His next was the surprising one of Director of the Cairo Zoo. At the age of 25 he made a remarkable camel journey in disguise from the Kharga Oasis to Siwa, a distance of over 300 miles, across a hazardous and treacherous desert. He was the first European traveller to enter Siwa, since the explorer Rohlfe in 1875. It was forbidden ground. The tribes were fierce and inhospitable and brutally hostile to strangers.

He was one of the first civilians in the Sudan after Kitchener captured Khartoum and carried out much of the early survey work there. He was appointed the first Governor of the Sinai in 1905. In the First World War he was one of the principal Intelligence Officers in the desert and in the Second World War was to come out of his retirement and serve Intelligence again.

At the end of the war he became Governor of the Western Desert and held that post until he retired in 1930.

Ramley Bey can count all the tribes of the desert as his friends. Complete master of their language and of their ways, he succeeded by peaceful persuasion in getting them to abandon their blood feuds and to come to his court at Burg El Arab, where, as the friend of both parties, he would listen to their endless arguments and give his judgment, which was always respected.

He did not want to talk to us about desert wars and romantic expeditions. He wanted to talk about his dreams and schemes for making the desert fruitful. Perhaps, he said wistfully, he would live long enough to see his ambition fulfilled, a fertile tract from Alexandria to the frontier. He said that he had been trying to persuade the authorities all his life of the military necessity for extending cultivation. Desert frontiers are wide open and an invitation to invaders, but tracts of cultivators would themselves be a natural defence system because the settlers, jealous for the safety of their land, would always be on the alert.

# CHAPTER SEVEN

## EXODUS BY TAXI

I T seems absurd: to walk out of the hotel, slip into a taxi, and drive off into the Sinai Desert to follow the footsteps of Moses and the Children of Israel. But that is how it happened.

The plan which had been made for me before my arrival in Egypt was that I should go east into the Sinai Desert to see a development scheme on the Wadhi El Arish, on the north coast of the peninsula. There was, however, a hitch.

For the first time on this mission, with its wholly pacific purpose, I was reminded that a state of war still existed in the Middle East. El Arish was part of the Egyptian defence system on the frontiers of Israel and the authorities did their best to dissuade me, and finally succeeded, from getting involved in something which was not my business. I was still determined, however, to go to the Biblical Wilderness and my discussions with Ali Shafei Bey, Director of Desert Irrigation, made me all the more anxious to do so.

Ali Shafei Bey turned out to be not only an engineer, but an archaeologist, who had made, for practical modern purposes, a study of the Exodus in the Bible. One of his great schemes is to irrigate the Wilderness of Etham, that part of the eastern desert of Egypt which figures in the early part of the Exodus and lies between the Nile and the Sinai Peninsula. This he schemed to do by restoring 'The River of the Sun', one of the former branches of the Nile which has disappeared, by a modern freshwater canal from the Nile near Cairo to the Mediterranean just west of Port Said.

As a water engineer, the 'Parting of the Waters' of the Red Sea had fascinated Ali Shafei Bey and, like most modern authorities, he was convinced that what was crossed was not the 'Red Sea' but the 'Reed Sea', that it is a Biblical mistranslation of *Yam Suph*, which means 'A Sea of Weeds'. This 'sea' probably lay in what is now the Canal Zone, north of the

Bitter Lakes. He himself had seen the waters piling up in marshlands in this area, and was able to show me photographs. The powerful dry wind acts like a *squeegee* (that rubber hoe-like implement which we use for cleaning pavements), forces the water back and, at the same time, dries out the marsh. While such a wind was prevailing, the Israelites could have crossed the marsh which would be dry enough for foot traffic, but when the wind abated the water would ebb back not to engulf and drown Pharaoh's armies, but to trap and bog-down their chariots.

His argument, from Bible sources, was that the Sinai, so far from being a hopeless, thirsty desert, was, as it still is, a relatively well-watered area. It is calculated that there is a waterhole, on the average, every fifteen miles—a day's march for the nomads. Even if the figures for the Exodus are dubious, the fact that a large community managed to sustain itself for forty years would indicate, in Biblical times, a reasonable food and water supply—not entirely explained by *manna* or by the spurting of water from the Rock of Horeb. No responsible modern authorities accept the figure (Numbers, Chapters 1 and 26) of 600,000 men in the flight from Egypt. This would mean a total of at least 2 or 3 million, including the women and children—which, by any standards of military organisation, is absurd. One modern version of the figures of the Exodus is that somehow a census which was taken in the time of David got mixed up with the account of the Exodus in later versions, as given by Greek scholars. A more reasonable figure is 600 *families*, which would make the numbers for whom Moses had to provide on the Exodus as between two and three thousand.

The Land of Goshen, where the Hebrews had sojourned for 400 years in the land of the Pharaohs, lay between the easternmost arm of the Delta and what is now the Suez Canal. Modern interpretation identifies the Pharaoh of the Oppression as Rameses II (1301-1234 B.C.). He was a great builder and for labour to construct two 'store cities' he conscripted the nomads of Goshen. The two cities, Ramses and Pithon, have been identified in the first instance with a town in the

Delta and in the second with a town not far from the Biblical
Succoth, near Lake Timsah, now part of the Suez Canal. By
this modern account Moses mustered the tribes and led them
through Succoth, south of Lake Timsah, across the *Reed Sea*
and into Sinai. By this evasive movement, say the scholars, he
avoided the road policed by Pharaoh's soldiers, the way of the
Philistines, which is the direct route into Palestine. What
perplexed one soldier who discussed this with me in Egypt
was why the southern route which he chose was any better,
because it was the road which led to the copper and turquoise
mines of the Pharaohs, with garrisons almost certainly in
control of the water wells en route.

It was no part of my mission to get involved with the
Biblical controversialists, but it was important to try to
understand what the historic wilderness had to teach by cross-
reference from the conditions 3,000 years ago to those of today.

That is how I came to hire Ianco and Pericles: I decided to
follow in the path of Moses by taxi.

Ianco is a Greek who served with the Hellenic Squadron of
the R.A.F. during the war and who now runs taxi No. 130
(Suez). Pericles, another Greek, has been driving in the Sinai
Desert for 25 years, and came along as pilot and relief driver. It
was absolutely essential to have two cars. One car might break
down and in the desolation of the Sinai might not be found for
weeks. Indeed, we spent quite a bit of time on our journey
through the Wilderness trying to find a party which had gone
off unescorted ten days before and had disappeared. The
second car carried, in the shape of spares, practically an entire
motor-car assembly, in addition to stores of petrol and
water.

The injunction was 'Keep Moving', because in the desert
one can never be quite sure whether the camel party coming
over the horizon, or loping down from the hills through the
passes, is friendly or hostile. In the past, when explorers went
by camel, the wise precaution was to put oneself under the
protection of a tribe in passing through its territory, and then
to be handed on to the next tribe, because, in the Sinai, the
sheikh of a tribe, and his followers, are made jointly respon-

sible for any murder or outrage committed by them or against someone under their protection.

This was a device usefully instituted by the Egyptian Government to maintain law and order in a remote region where only the ancient laws of an eye for an eye, or a tooth for a tooth, apply. Within and between the tribes, it is not a capital offence to commit a murder, but it will lead to a blood feud in which the members of the victim's family can take revenge. Then there will be fresh reprisals. To prevent accumulative slaughter, the tribes were persuaded to submit to arbitration and a life can be commuted into a fine, or compensation levied from the murderer's tribe. Where a stranger is involved (and it was a poor consolation to me when I learned it) the Government will exact the penalty from the whole tribe. This system of corporate justice has been extremely effective, but it is not the kind of law that one can argue with a trigger-happy Bedouin 100 miles from anywhere.

So the safest way is to 'keep moving' and to get out of range of any approaching band. When, as frequently happened, one or other of the cars got trapped in loose sand, there was a frantic scurry and everyone rallied round the boulders, or pawed the sand like dogs hunting for a bone, to get a grip for the spinning wheels. On the whole trip we were only once overtaken and  hastily established friendly relations by dishing out packets of cigarettes.

Nothing could have been more prosaic than our exodus out of Egypt into Sinai. We started off from our hotel at Suez after a night disturbed by Scottish Tommies singing 'I belang tae Glesga' and after a meal of bacon and eggs. We drove to the ship canal, only to find that the ferry had broken down. While Ianco and Pericles, with noisy exasperation, insisted upon helping the mechanics to replace the broken crankshaft, one could only sit and watch the ships go past. From a distance, with the canal below eye level, and apparently nothing but a solid expanse of desert, the sight of a ship apparently ploughing through the sand is an amusing illusion. But even that, after three hours, can get tedious.

With loud cheers and a great scurrying the ferryboat got under way and in three minutes we were in Sinai.

The road across the flat plain was disappointingly good. Somehow it did not seem proper that we should be bowling along, in the path of Moses, at 50 miles an hour. Our first stop was at an army post, where we had to produce our special permits and submit to an interrogation which was not entirely red tape, because the military had to satisfy themselves as to our possible movements in case it should be necessary to send out a search party.

A few miles further south we came to the Well of Moses. This is a large oasis of date palms and sparkling pools as inviting as a swimming-bath. Today it looks across the gleaming aluminium oil tanks on the other side of the Gulf of Suez and at the ships queueing up to enter the canal. It is about the one patch of greenery that travellers coming up the Gulf see in Sinai and it only serves to heighten the impression of sandy desolation. These sand dunes, however, extend only about 20 miles from the coast, as far as the escarpments of the gravel plateau, which stretches 100 miles to the Palestine frontier and 150 miles to the south.

Presently the macadam road switched us into an oil-track— just desert soil flattened by bulldozers, with the dirt bound by crude oil instead of tar. This method of surfacing is handy (if messy) because here in the Biblical Wilderness are modern intrusions—oil derricks invading the Old Testament. Any inquiries about the extent of these operations and of the oilfield, which must be considerable, are coldly discouraged. But since we were not blindfolded we could not miss seeing the activities of the oil camps and the presence of the American oil men.

'And Moses led Israel onward from the Red Sea and they

went out into the Wilderness of Shur; and they went three days into the Wilderness and found no water. And when they came to Marah they could not drink the waters of Marah, for they were bitter; therefore the name of it was called *Marah* (Bitterness). And the people murmured against Moses saying, What shall we drink? And he cried unto the Lord: and the Lord showed him a tree and he cast it into the waters and the waters were made sweet'.

(Exodus, Chapter 15).

If, as is suggested nowadays, *Marah* is *Ain Hawarah,* I can testify that the waters are still sweet.

Further south we came to Abu Zenima where we had to report at another Army post, because here we were leaving the coast and striking into the mountains. Abu Zenima is quite an industrial centre, because it is the smelting place and the port for the manganese mines. Huge tips of grey manganese tower above the village and a narrow gauge railway runs into the hills, to the mines.

Close by here is Gharandal, which some experts identify as Elim, where were *'twelve springs of water and three score and ten palm trees'* (Exodus, Chapter 15). I did not count, but the present oasis could be consistent with that.

The next question, if we were accepting this southern route of the Israelites, was the location of the Wilderness of Sin. That depends on the identification of Dophkah. Since in the Hebrew original *Dophkah* means 'smelting', it is likely that it refers to the copper mining in the mountains which we were entering. This is reinforced by the presence in Sinai of Jethro, the Midianite, Moses' father-in-law. The Midianites belonged to what is now the Hedjaz, in the Arabian Desert on the other side of the Gulf of Akaba, the eastern boundary of the Sinai peninsula. But there was a branch of the Midianites, the *Kenites,* which means 'metalsmiths', to which Jethro belonged, who probably worked the Sinai mines.

The 'road' which we were taking along the dried river beds of the *wadhis* into the mountains was no more than the tracks of those who had been there before us—the idea being that if they had got through, perhaps we could. But since the winds keep shifting the sands, this was often a snare, and not once but dozens of times the trail would lead us into a sand trap, in which a car would be as helpless as a beetle on its back. That was where the second car had to come to the rescue.

This was the area of the granite mountains, surely one of the extraordinary geological spectacles in the world. Bare of vegetation and weathered down to bedrock, the layers of rocks are clearly exposed. The seams are of every colour, from jet-black to snow-white; from the colour of the copper beech to mulberry green; blue and grey, orange and purple; all the colours of an artist's paint box or of the rainbow. One great sweep of mountains I christened 'The Rainbow Mountains', not only because of the colours but because in some great convulsion the seams have been folded into an arc—a petrified rainbow.

If in our contact with the ancient mines we had indeed visited Dophkah, our next stage must be 'The Wilderness of Sin'. Without any argument with the archaeologists and Biblical disputants, I am quite prepared to accept it. If it is a 'Wilderness of Sin', it is also a 'Wilderness of Penance'—a vast expanse of unrelieved desolation. It so oppressed us that Ianco, the irrepressible, defiantly switched on the car radio and we journeyed through Sin to the strains of 'Mademoiselle de Paris', and American swing, while the falcons wheeled overhead.

Then even the trails which pass as roads ceased and Pericles negotiated sand traps and rocky pitfalls like a pilot dodging shoals—not always successfully. There were occasions when we had to get out and assist the taxi down flights of stairs carved by nature in the rocks. At one point we were trapped, it seemed hopelessly so, in loose sand with the skeleton of a camel picked clean by carrion a few feet away, to remind us of what can happen in the desert.

As we moved into the narrowing passes of the mountains, the scenery changed from the monotony of the Wilderness of Sin into a riot of queer, natural architecture. There was a stretch of limestone formations, sand-blasted into grotesque shapes—weather-sculptured pyramids, domes and minarets,

AN OASIS
DIES :
A grove of
date palms,
flag - staff
high, is
buried in
the advanc-
ing dunes.

AN OASIS
IS BORN:
From man-
made arte-
sian wells,
water is
brought by
concrete
channels to
thirsty, but
fertile des-
ert.

3000 B.C.: Persian qanat, or horizontal well. Such channels date back 5000 years. Man-made they sometimes stretch 20 miles underground.

1950 A.D.: Outlet of modern pumping station, in the Algerian desert, bringing water from new plumbed depths.

basilicas and fortresses and escarpments hanging in curtain-like folds.

In the Wadhi Mukatteb (The Valley of Writings) we stopped to examine the Sinaitic inscriptions. On fallen blocks of granite are writings and drawings which for long confused historians. The drawings include crude horses, camels and ibex and inscriptions which beat the experts for centuries but are now believed to be the work of Nabatean camel herds.

The Nabateans were a Semitic race who flourished in the 500 years before Christ and whose capital was that remarkable place Petra on the east side of the Wadhi Araba in the Negev. At Petra houses, temples and tombs were hewn in the soft multi-coloured sandstone cliffs. Flights of stairways cut into the rock led up every hill. Beautiful murals still adorn the interiors. They were a highly civilised race. They pushed a border of cultivated land far into deserts where the rainfall would have defeated lesser men. Their systems of reservoirs, underground cisterns, wadhi-dams and aqueducts are an example to modern engineers today. Their shepherds and camel herds ranged deep into the Sinai, even into these remote mountains of the south, and as proof of a literacy, shared even by the herdsmen, we have these rock inscriptions.

Basically the language is a form of Aramaic, the language of the Chaldeans and the Assyrians of Mesopotamia, but the inscriptions are mixed with Kufic (the language of a Babylonian city) and Greek. It was probably this mixture which baffled the experts, but modern deciphering can make some excuse for them—they were probably looking for something very profound, perhaps even for the origin of the Law. It appears, however, that these were no more than the kind of scratchings which trippers make on trees or on ancient monuments—'Remember Zailu, son of Waila'; or 'I, Lupus, a soldier, wrote this with my own hand'. As C. S. Jarvis points out in *Yesterday* and *Today in the Sinai,* it is rather like expecting the historians 2,000 years from now to make sense out of a present-day scratching like 'Coronach, a snip for the Derby', or some even ruder inscriptions.

It was late in the afternoon before we reached the Wadhi

H

Feiran which, some claim, was Rephidim, where the Israelites fought with Amalek. Feiran is a lush oasis, even today, and all around the mountains are pitted with abandoned caves in which at one time or another 6,000 hermits lived. The present-day hermit is a youthful Greek monk, with a spade-beard, who lives in a one-man monastery. He greeted us with great warmth, partly because he was a friend of Ianco's in his worldly days, but also because we brought him his first supply of cigarettes for weeks. In spite of all the embracing and back-slapping and badinage, he was very earnest in his attempt to persuade us not to go on and risk being caught by nightfall in the mountains. We were anxious, however, to get to Mount Sinai Monastery that night, and anyway, there were a couple of hours still before sunset.

That is where we were wrong. By our watches it might be true but in these high mountains the sun, of course, 'sets' before it reaches the horizon at sea level. The mountains rise up like shutters and when the sun drops behind them, bury the valleys in shadow. That happened to us within half-an-hour of leaving the hermit. It was like climbing a chimney—and a freezing one at that. What was more, we were groping for a road which, to say the least of it, was ill-defined, and for the most part did not exist. The car lights were treacherous, because they made sliding gravel and slippery rocks look deceptively sound.

Dying a thousand deaths, we crawled up to the heights from which, by the light of a crescent moon lying on its back, we saw Wadhi El Sheikh, a wide expanse where the Israelites were supposed to have worshipped the Golden Calf. We were now in the Mountains of the Ten Commandments—holy ground of three religions, Jewish, Christian and Moslem—with Moses Mount looming ahead and, somewhere at its foot, the monastery for which we were making. The descent was even more nerve-racking than the climb.

Presently taxi No. 130 (Suez) took a last desperate lunge through the shadows and jolted to a standstill. This time it was not at the usual edge of a precipice but outside the fortress walls of Mount Sinai. Ianco, who had long switched off

'Mademoiselle de Paris' and had said a lot of prayers in these mountains where the Israelites trembled before Jehovah's wrath, shouted in triumph and relief, and the Mountain of Moses echoed back a rumbling reproach. Pericles sounded his horn which the megaphone of the mountains turned into a Joshua's trumpet. But the fortress walls did not respond. There was no answering glimmer of light and we were faced with the grim prospect of spending the night in the open, with an icy wind funnelling past the Rock of the Golden Calf.

Defying the reproachful echoes, we kept on shouting and hooting until a lantern procession of turbaned figures came from a cluster of huts outside the wall. The shrouded figures were the Moslem servants of the monastery—a strange race called the *Gebeliya*. They are not Arabs in origin, but are descended from slaves imported from Wallachia (Rumania) in the 6th century. They were never accepted into the safety of the monastery they served and could only survive the hostility of the Bedouins by turning Mohammedan in the 7th century.

I know all that now but at the time all I knew was that they were friendly human beings in bleak, cold and threatening surroundings. Somehow they contrived to rouse the guest-master of the monastery. With untrimmed beard and unshorn locks, which had come out of their bun, the monk gave us a cordial welcome as wayfarers, despite the hour—long past the bedtime of monks who start their devotions at 3 a.m.

Leading the way with a hurricane lamp, he helped us across the boulders until we found a small concealed entrance in the walls of this fortress-monastery. This entrance is just six feet high and three feet broad, and there is a succession of three massive doors, with iron plates and bolts and loopholes for archers.

The key with which he undid it was over a foot long. The first door gave on to a dark passage with loopholes through which the defenders could thrust spears or arrows while any attackers were trying to force the second equally massive door. The second door let us into a passage at right-angles leading to the third door. This intricate system of entry is contrived within the thickness of the wall, which encloses the entire monastery and is 280 feet long by 250 feet in breadth, of enormous blocks of granite five feet square. At each corner there is a round tower. The only other entrance to the monastery is by boatswain's chair, a sling which is hoisted to the battlements by windlass.

We followed the guest-master's lamp through the tunnel of the walls and up the granite paved ramps and winding stairs of the monastery township. Five storeys up we came to the gallery of cells on the battlements, where we were to be accommodated for the night. We were given the freedom of a sitting-room, decorated with British Sunday-school lithographs of the Exodus theme and by magazine photographs of Britain's King George and Queen Elizabeth, King Paul of the Hellenes and the Mohammedan King Farouk of Egypt. We were also allowed to use the kitchen to cook the food which we had brought with us, and one of the *Gebeliyas* was called in to help. On a massive stone stove which looked like an altar, he made a fire of tamarisk and sweet-smelling shrubs, so that our spaghetti tasted of incense. If our tea had been made of attar of roses, it would still have been acceptable after our eventful day, which, by way of compensation for all our fears, had given us a terrific appetite.

I slept badly. It was not the meal, the whitewashed austerity of the cell, or the hardness of the straw mattress. It was the gale. It bellowed and moaned and boomed amongst the mountains. I got up and went out on to the battlements in the middle of the night and in the uncanny moonlight watched the clouds pile up behind the crags of the Mount of Moses. And I realised why the Old Testament Jehovah was the God of Wrath. Everything was angry—the wind, the landscape, the clouds.

I crept back to bed but at 3 a.m. my storm-tossed dreams were punctuated by a strained, muffled sound, a dull booming. It was a monk, on the campanile of the church, within 20 feet of my cell, beating a baton of wood with a wooden mallet to summon the monks to their 3 a.m. devotions.

In daylight the monastery was a less sombre but no less extraordinary place. Alongside that bell tower of the Church of St. Catherine, separated by a few feet, was a mosque with its minaret, a Moslem mosque inside a Christian monastery.

The monastery is a mixture of everything from patriarchal times until today. There is the Well of Jethro, where Jethro reintroduced Moses to his wife Zipporah and their two sons. It stands in a courtyard with a modern pumphead. Nearby is the Burning Bush. It is now enclosed in a chapel, and on entering one follows the Biblical injunction and removes one's shoes. There is no evidence of the Burning Bush in the chapel. The monks who, with their predecessors, have kept the candles alight for at least 1,500 years, assure you that the roots still exist under the altar. Outside the chapel, enclosed by a fence, is a bush which has sprouted (they will tell you) from the original roots, which grows with perennial green leaves, alongside Aaron's rod which *'budded, and brought forth buds, and bloomed blossoms, and yielded almonds'*. (Numbers, Chap. 17, 9.)

In the lavishly ornamented chapel of St. Catherine is the casket containing the remains of the martyr who was broken on the wheel, beheaded and quartered and who was miraculously carried by angels to St. Catherine's Mount in the Sinai. In her chapel are two massive and ornate silver caskets which, on two separate occasions, were sent by Czars of Russia to transport relics of the martyr to Russia, but whenever her remains were taken from the original casket, they miraculously returned to it. So the bones of St. Catherine are still there. And so are the Czars' caskets.

Mount Sinai Monastery is a treasure-house of the early Christian Church. In its library, a recent, modern reconstruction, are over 3,000 manuscripts, most of them beautifully illuminated and of great age. Some of the most valuable have been ruined because pages have been torn out, and some of the most precious are not there. The monastery was always a hospitable place and the monks were trusting. Visitors were given free access to the treasures and were not always scrupulous. According to the white-bearded Sacristan, a German called Tischendorf visited the monastery in 1844 and walked off with the famous *Codex Sinaiticus*, which dates back to A.D. 400 and is a Greek version of the Old Testament (including the *Apocrypha*) and the most complete version of the New Testament. It was sold to the Czar and was acquired from the Soviet Government by the British Museum for £100,000.

Among all these Christian treasures there is a Moslem script which the monks value very highly. And so they should. It has helped to save them from martyrdom for 1,500 years. In its way it has been as great a protection as the massive fortress which Justinian built in A.D. 530 to enclose the community and the Church which had been built in A.D. 340 by the Mother of the Emperor Constantine.

As a fortress it is massive but militarily unsound, because the mountains rise sheer above it and expose the defenders to missiles from above. Justinian is reported to have executed the engineers who misplaced it. Nevertheless, assisted by a roll of parchment it saved the monks of Mount Sinai from the fate that overtook all the other convents and hermitages, the ruins of which can be seen around the Mountains of the Law Giving, including the 6,000 hermits of Wadhi Feiran.

As the monks unroll this parchment, it is as well not to look incredulous and sceptical but to accept, at its face value, the account of its origins. According to this account, a young camel driver at the beginning of the 7th century was lost in these mountains and sought refuge in the monastery. With remarkable foresight the monks recognised him as one who in years to come was to be the Prophet Mohammed and in return for their hospitality secured from him a scroll which ordered his followers-to-be never to violate the monastery of Mount Sinai. The young camel driver could not sign the document but left his sign-manual, an ink-print of his hand. The document which they show you is not the original, which was confiscated by a Turkish sultan, but it is claimed to be a facsimile. How they managed to reproduce the Prophet's ink-print a thousand years after his death would be a matter of some interest to scientists (and to Scotland Yard), which I did not dare to broach. At all events, even as a copy, it has served its purpose and the community of Mount Sinai has been safe and on good terms with the Moslem Bedouins.

Every day Arab families from the surrounding tribes, under an ancient agreement, come to the monastery to receive their ration of unleavened bread, which is baked in the cavernous bakehouse of the monastery and lowered in baskets from the battlements. At one time the resident monks of Mount Sinai must have formed a very large community. It is still a large community—but not at Mount Sinai. There are 14 monks in the monastery, and 40 in Cairo, where lives the Patriarch of Mount Sinai. The community also has rich establishments in Cyprus and elsewhere.

In spite of its gloomy position in the ravines, where the sun disappears at 1 o'clock in the afternoon, the monastery is well provided for. A stream flows through the valley—but not from the Rock of Horeb which Moses struck with his rod and from which water gushed. The rock, which is now pointed out as Moses' Rock, is dry. The springs on the mountains irrigate olive groves and vineyards and orchards. The gardens adjoining the monastery itself are sheltered by cypresses and olive trees and produce oranges and abundant vegetables.

From the lands of the Little Monastery, at Wadhi Feiran, where we met the solitary monk, the *Gebeliyan* retainers of the monastery produce wheat for the bread and it was a surprising sight to see the monks, in the middle of the Sinai, dining off lobsters. These had been fetched by the servants from the Gulf of Akaba—a return journey by camel of 36 hours. If the monks want to post a letter or send a telegram, a young *Gebeliyan*, with a gourd of water, a loaf of bread and a handful of olives, will blithely set off on foot on a two-days' journey across the mountains to Tor on the Gulf of Suez, with as little fuss or preparation as if he were going to the pillar-box at the end of the street.

Among the 14 monks in this great monastery was one who turned out to be a war-time 'buddy' of Ianco, an ex-member of the Hellenic Squadron of the R.A.F.

The peninsula at Mount Sinai supports about 20,000 Bedouins, who, as nomads, are quite content with the life of the Patriarchs—grazing their flocks and herds and, for their bread, tilling any patch of land which may be convenient.

It is quite wrong to think of Sinai as a waterless desert or as hungry land. Even the Biblical accounts of the Israelites being rescued from famine by manna and quails, referred to episodes. Moses sustained the Children of Israel for more than a generation in this 'wilderness'.

The manna one can still find on the leaves of the tamarisk. This manna is a sugary deposit *'and it was like coriander seed, white; and the taste of it was like wafers made with honey'.* It is produced by an aphis, which lives on the tamarisk and in the early morning the white deposit falls off on to the ground and may drift with the wind. It has to be collected at the time of the dew, otherwise, as in the Bible, it melts with the sun. The quails which *'at even came and covered the camp'* are a regular phenomenon. In the months of September and October, clouds of quails, migrating south, collapse in Northern Sinai tired out by their Mediterranean crossing and can be easily gathered by hand. Nowadays they are not found in Southern Sinai, but are still abundant on the sandy flats of the north. This has led some of the authorities, notably Major C. S. Jarvis, who was Governor of Sinai, to dispute that the Flight from Egypt ever turned south. He argues that the quails, among other evidence, show that the Israelites went along the north coast, and that they ultimately established themselves, while recruiting their strength for the invasion of Canaan, at *Ain Gedeirat,* near Kosseima, close to the existing Palestine frontier.

Today, if Ali Shafei Bey and his colleagues of the Egyptian Irrigation Service had their way and were able to develop their schemes, Sinai, and its Wilderness, could support a multitude even greater than the Exodus.

# CHAPTER EIGHT

## LAND OF THE ARABIAN NIGHTS

AT one point of the journey through Sinai we were within 60 miles of the place to which I wanted to get in the Negev, in the Wilderness of Zin (not *Sin* which is another spot altogether). In order to reach it, however, I had to travel not 60 miles but 2,500 miles.

Even an international mission could not make it possible for me to cross 'the frontiers of Egypt into Israel. If my passport had had an Israeli visa, no Arab State would have admitted me and no Egyptian frontier guard would have allowed me to pass. So, although Israel was, like the Arab countries, a Member State of Unesco, in the name of which I was travelling, I had to return to Cairo, fly due north across the Delta over the Mediterranean, keeping well away from the Palestine coast, until we were abreast of Beirut in the Arab League State of Lebanon. Then we turned east and flew to Damascus in Syria, across the desert to Baghdad, over the hump to Persia, then we turned round and flew back to Cyprus and from Cyprus into Palestine and the Negev. True, I was going eventually to Iraq and Persia, but, sensibly, my route should have lain through the Negev and eastwards through Trans-Jordan (or Hashimite Jordan as it has become). As it was, I was never to cross the Jordan, because, although the Israelis, to make life simple for me and avoid the duplicity of a 'dummy' passport, had waived all formalities, the immigration officer at Lydda, while my attention was elsewhere, absent-mindedly stamped my passport recording my arrival at Lydda. That slip cancelled my passport and my Hashimite visa.

The nearest I was to get to Abdullah's kingdom was to stand on the balcony of the King David Hotel in Jerusalem and exchange waves with an Arab Legion sentry on the walls of the Old City less than fifty yards away.

But no political difficulties could sour the pleasurable anti-

cipation with which I journeyed to Iraq. Here I was going to
the country of Haroun Al Raschid and the Arabian Nights to
Babylon, to the land that was the cradle of a great civilisation.
To assist the illusion I had booked a room at the Sinbad Hotel,
on the banks of the Tigris.

If I had dreamed of oriental spendour and the colourful
romanticism of the Baghdad of the Arabian Nights, I was
bound to be disappointed by the modern city, where little
survives of the glamorous past.

By the way of consolation, one could try to recapture some of
it in the *souk,* or bazaar, and in the museum. In the narrow
alleys of the *souk* one can find some picturesqueness in the fire-
lit booths of the smiths and the colourful displays of the carpet
merchants. Even in Persia, which we always associate with
oriental carpets, the displays cannot equal the variety of the
Baghdad bazaars. The explanation is that the pilgrims to
Mecca from the mountains to the north and east—from Kur-
distan, from Tabriz, from Kerman, Ispahan and all the places
famous for their carpet work—converge on Baghdad. By the
time they get to the Tigris their rations are giving out and they
have to lay in fresh supplies. Their currency is carpets. Some,
with foresight, may bring carpets to finance themselves in the
ordinary way of trade, but many of the Faithful are destitute
and have to sell their prayer rugs on which they have lavished
special care and skills and for which even the sharp traders of
Baghdad will pay big prices, knowing they will fetch even
bigger.

My impression of Baghdad was dimmed by a dust storm.
At high noon the sun above the city was blotted out by what
might have been the thickest form of the proverbial London
fog, only this was not fog but dust as fine as face powder, borne
on a southern wind from what may have been the Garden of
Eden. On top of this dust storm came the rain and the dust
was sluiced out of the atmosphere as liquid mud. It was most
unpleasant being drenched with mud from the sky, by a slime
on which the barefoot boys made skids, like ice slides, along
the footways, and which painted even the most luxurious lim-
ousines with a complete khaki camouflage.

This grit, which I had for lunch in Twentieth Century Baghdad, is the dust, or wind scourings, of the soil, which has smothered the evidence of both primitive and highly advanced Mesopotamian culture which can be dated back 10,000 years. It blows from the Persian Gulf across Sumeria, Ur of the Chaldees (Abraham's birthplace) and Babylonia; and since Dr. Naji Beg Al-Asil, Iraqi Director of Antiquities, claims that if the Garden of Eden existed anywhere, it existed in a part of Southern Mesopotamia, now desert, the soil I was eating was presumbly that of Eden (*Edenam* is a Sumerian word meaning 'garden').

Even if Eden was not in the south, as he claimed, but, as others suggest, in the north among the source waters of the Euphrates, I could still have been eating its soil as dust blown from the south, because the entire land area in the Tigris Euphrates basin south of Baghdad (now 350 miles from the sea) has been built up from silt rubbed off the mountains in the north. About 4,000 B.C. the Persian Gulf extended north of Baghdad almost to Samara. In Sumerian times, i.e. the days of Abraham, Ur, his birthplace, was on the coast, instead of being as it is now 150 miles from the sea.

I had only to look out of my window of the Sinbad Hotel to realise how this had happened. The Tigris is so heavy with mud that it does not ripple, it pleats.

The fate of the successive civilisations which flourished and died in Mesopotamia is almost entirely the history of the collapse of irrigation systems. Wars may have helped but they were part of the process of the collapse of these systems. If an invader killed or carried off a population, the irrigation systems could not be maintained and, in their collapse, were likely in the end to destroy the empire of the conqueror.

Central and Southern Mesopotamia has a rainfall too low for cultivation, but it has abundant water—in fact, too much water. Every year the banks of the Tigris and the Euphrates above Baghdad have to be deliberately burst in order to drain off the flood waters which would swamp the city; and in the south, between Kut and Basra, are the water-buffalo swamps —the choked 'drains' of the two rivers.

All over the deserts of Mesopotamia are the buried remains of once flourishing cities, and in conjunction with them the mounds which marked the courses of the ancient canals. In the remote centuries the hydraulic engineers of those far-from primitive peoples cleverly used the curious geography of the Euphrates and the Tigris. Above what is now Baghdad the bed of the Euphrates is higher than that of the Tigris and south of Baghdad towards Kut-El-Amara (famous as a besieged city in the First World War) the Tigris is higher than the Euphrates. The irrigation engineers were able on this account to produce canals by downhill flow between the two rivers. The extent of this canal system is quoted as evidence in support of the claim that Babylonia was the great granary of the ancient world, but, as Abdul-Amir-Al-Uzri, Iraqi Director of Irrigation, pointed out to me, this is probably misleading because these irrigated areas were not all working at the same time. Nevertheless, they add up into a very impressive sum of what was and could be again.

The existing courses of these canals are traced not by ditches but by dykes—by high mounds. When the canals silted they had to be dredged by hand, by throwing the mud on to the banks. When the banks became about ten feet high, the shovellers could not throw any higher; it became simpler to dig new canals. This chopping and changing, however, was disturbing to the flow of the rivers and every now and then forced them out of their courses. For instance, on one side of Babylon runs the 'Hillah Canal', and, enclosing it on the other, is the Euphrates. It is generally assumed that the 'canal' was man-made, but the local experts now are prepared to argue that the 'canal' was the original river bed and that the present 'Waters of Babylon' was the man-made diversion.

This recalls the story of the Feast of Belshazzar. Belshazzar was the Babylonian general of the 6th century B.C., who was defending the city against Cyrus and the Persians. The garrison laughed when Cyrus began to dig a deep trench around the city in order, as they thought, to starve them out, whereas there were twenty years' provisions within the walls. Cyrus chose the night of the feast when the mysterious fingers wrote on the walls of the banqueting hall '*Mene, mene, tekel, upharsin*' (God has numbered thy kingdom and found it wanting) and diverted the Euphrates into the trench. They then invaded the city across the dry river bed.

The Euphrates, always being disturbed in its bed, got its revenge. It reduced the neighbourhood of Babylon to marshes. The marshes bred malarial mosquitoes. I stood where the Waters of Babylon join the Hillah Canal at the spot where Alexander the Great died of malaria. Death and disease produced by the marsh mosquitoes crippled the population, so that they were not able to work the irrigation systems or till the fields, and so the process of collapse speeded up. With some justification, it can be claimed that it was the mosquito, and not the Mongols, which in the end destroyed Babylon.

Today all that one can grasp is the magnitude of Babylon as it once was and the extent of the remains. The prophecy of Isaiah has certainly been fulfilled: 'I shall sweep it with the besom of destruction, saith the Lord of Hosts.'

The glory that was the Babylon of Nebuchadnezzar has certainly departed. Apart from his wars and his subjugation and carrying off the Jews into captivity, the chief work of Nebuchadnezzar was the enlargement and beautifying of Babylon to surpass Nineveh in architectural glory. He repaired the great Temple of Marduk and erected the vast Imperial Palace on top of which, rising terrace upon terrace, were the Hanging Gardens, one of 'the Seven Wonders of the World'. He reconstructed the Tower of Babel. The 'Tower' was a *ziggurat,* a pyramid structure—not for the dead, as in the case of Egypt, but for the living—on the topmost tower of which was a spacious temple. Such *ziggurats* were a regular feature of the Mesopotamian civilisation. In the *ziggurats* of Eridu, in the south near Ur, the Iraqis have recently excavated 14 prehistoric temples one on top of the other.

It had been my intention to go to Eridu, the site which has established the existence of a well-advanced culture in 4,000 B.C. It is so old that it accounts for the Sumerian legend of the Creation, which says '*The land was still sea when Eridu was made.*' In addition to the 14 stacked temples, they have found the remains which include settlements which are earlier by nearly 500 years than any city civilisations previously discovered. The houses in these settlements of 6,000 years ago were identical in construction with the huts which the water-buffalo herdsmen build in the marshes of the south.

I was dissuaded from going to Eridu because it would be a waste of time; there would be nothing to see. Three seasons' work of excavation has been buried again in the dust. Each year, when the archæologists came back, they had to start their diggings by exhuming the modern house which was their headquarters and which was regularly swallowed up. Having seen the destruction wreaked by modern archæologists at Babylon, I think it is just as well that the desert is so reluctant to give up Eridu.

Babylon was mercifully buried until about 50 years ago when German archæologists opened the site and exposed what was left of the fabulous city. They removed all that was movable to the museums of the west, chipping off the coloured tiles and *bas-reliefs* and leaving the rest as 'quarries' from which builders could carry off the masonry and sculptures for use in modern construction. It was downright robbery and so thorough that Babylon is little more than a ground plan of the city-that-was. It is some comfort that present-day diggings are carefully supervised and protected and scientifically carried out.

Like so many other travellers in Mesopotamia, I was in danger of falling under the spell of the ancient civilisations and might have spent months or years touring the mounds of the old cities \of which hundreds exist. My concern with archæology, however, was confined to the lessons it had to teach us, from the past, for the recovery and cultivation of the deserts. If one glances at the map of these ancient sites, it is easy to conclude that some disaster of climate overtook them and changed the prosperously fertile region into desert.

The story of the Flood is too persistent in ancient accounts not to have some basis. The Hebrew account in the Old Testament is closely paralleled in Babylonian documents which, in turn, are based on Sumerian sources of around 3,000 B.C. The ark in the Babylonian version grounded on the Zagros Mountains, north-east of Babylon, while according to the Old Testament it landed on Ararat in Armenia. The ancient civilisations, which persist as ruins, were not, however, drowned but dried out.

It would be easy to assume that in the past 5,000 years the climate of Mesopotamia has changed and the decline of the rainfall has reduced it to an arid zone. This is difficult to square with the facts. The evidence of all these cities now stranded in the deserts is that they were sustained by irrigation and by methods entirely consistent with a rainfall and conditions similar to what now exists. The conditions which forced the abandonment of cities were most likely due not to a change in climate but to human intervention. There is evidence that the Tigris and the Euphrates, and the lesser rivers in the area, changed their courses and left cities high and dry. Even this can be explained by the development and decline of canal systems. For example, before the time of Rim-Sin, the Euphrates came west of Ur, reaching the Persian Gulf near Eridu, but Rim-Sin straightened the course of the river so that it passed by Ur, while the people of Erech to the north dammed the river to irrigate their region. Eridu and another city, Lagash, were both separated from the water and perished for lack of it.

This interference, in turn, destroyed Erech, left it in the waterless desert and silted up the Euphrates, built up the soil which now separates Ur and Eridu from the sea, and made the river, with the Tigris, merely a tributary of the Shatt-Al-Arab.

Babylonia, the Graveyard of the Lost Civilisations, can become again one of the richest gardens of the world—if we are prepared to read aright the lessons and warnings of the past. We cannot afford to feel superior about these Ancients. The Middle East was the nursery of much of our western culture, of our religion, of our philosophy, of our writing, of our mathematics, and of our money system and commerce. When we acknowledge our debt to Greece and Rome, we have to extend our debt to the civilisations from which they borrowed so much.

It is with proper humility, for example, we should remember that the Chaldeans were the founders of astronomy as an exact science. They kept observations continuously for over 360 years. One Chaldean astronomer in the millennium before Christ was able to calculate the length of the year at 365 days, 6 hours, 15 minutes and 41 seconds—a measurement which the modern telescope has proved to be only 26 *minutes 26 seconds too long*. His calculations of the diameter of the face of the moon were far more accurate than those of Copernicus, whom we tend to accept as the founder of modern astronomy.

Three months before my visit, in the excavations of Tel-El-Harmel, near Baghdad, they found clay tablets which proved that an ancient mathematician had worked out the theorems of Euclid (300 B.C.) two thousand years before him. These mathematical tablets were only a tiny fraction of the 2,500 'books' in the library. The clay literature included textbooks of geography, history, astronomy and botany, and indicated that this site was a great university. In the days of the Old Testament Patriarchs, Hammurabi (1728-1686 B.C.) produced a code of laws, themselves an adaptation of even older Sumerian laws and customs, and which are similar to the secular (as distinct from the Divine) Hebrew laws of the Old Testament.

Included in the Hammurabic code were bye-laws on irrigation such as: '*If a man open his canal for irrigation and neglect it and the water spoil a neighbour's field, he shall measure out unto him grain in proportion to the neighbour's fields.'*

If we can accept so much from the wisdom of the Ancients, we can accept also a great deal of their technology. What we have today are the mechanised slaves to replace the human slave-labour on which they had to rely and which they had to collect by conquest and expatriation—like the removal of the Jews from Palestine into Babylon. Even in the respect of modern machine power, the Middle East can salvage its past by invoking an even older world and the oil of primæval times which lies beneath its deserts. The great oilfields of Mosul lie below Nineveh and the buried empire of the ancient Assyrians.

There is an old Iraqi saying *Once upon a time, the cock which crowed in Mosul could be heard in Basra.* It would be a shrill cock which could be heard over a distance of 700 miles. What it means is that the areas of cultivation were once so closely settled that one cock could start a relay of crowing right down the valleys to the sea. There are schemes—on paper at least—which would make that possible again.

The first essential, however, is flood control, both of the Euphrates and of the Tigris. The floods are becoming un-manageable and the crude method of just bursting the banks to prevent the water from swamping Baghdad means drowning lands which could be usefully productive.

One scheme which is almost completed, at Habbaniyah, will divert the Euphrates into a freshwater lake, and, when the flood is excessively high, will carry the excess into the salt depression of Bahar-Il-Milh. The freshwater can be canalised back into the river from the lake and, as a regulated flow, can double the amount of water, in the summer months, in the Euphrates. This can maintain and increase irrigation during the dry season and multiply the crops.

On the Tigris, near Samarra, there is an even bigger project to divert the spate into Wadhi Tharthar. There is a third scheme for a great reservoir on the Diyala, designed to develop a large area of cultivation—for a start, 300,000 acres—between the Tigris and the Diyala River. These three schemes

I

will cost about £14,000,000, which is not a lot of money to spend on redeeming the past and providing for the future. There are other great schemes still to be approved and financed which would enable the great marshes in the south to be drained and brought into production.

The effects of such developments can profoundly affect not only the economic, but the social life of Iraq. Like all Arab countries, Iraq has a complicated system of land tenure. It is a country of great landlords owning hundreds of thousands of acres apiece. Since cultivation is seasonal, the landlords can take advantage of the habits of the desert tribes who, as nomads, prefer a pastoral existence, but who at the time of ploughing and harvesting hire their services to the landowners, who bargain with the sheikhs on a seasonal contract. This leads to all kinds of bad practices which the Iraqi Government would like to break. The landowners are too powerful for land reforms to be attempted by breaking up the great estates, but it can be done by creating new land, persuading the nomads to settle and so depriving the landowners of this source of cheap labour.

Such a scheme of settlement is being carried out near Kut, where land is being reclaimed and irrigated and parcelled out 100 acres per farmer. It takes the form of co-operative farming, with the Ministry of Agriculture helping with the equipment, seeds and marketing. As an oil country, the emphasis is on mechanisation.

Behind these schemes are big experimental stations. One near Baghdad, at Abu-Ghraid, is a 12,000 acre centre for studying soil, breeding animals and plants, and adapting imported varieties to the country's requirements. There one can see the range of possibilities—wheat, barley, oats, linseed, cotton, ground-nuts, maize and sugar-cane. In this area of the rivers, grain as we know it today was first developed from the grasses, but in the progress of the centuries, the native varieties have changed for the worse, and the aim of the experts is to give to the farmers the best of present-day world experience.

Outside the river basins are the vast tracts of steppe-land,

and one of the aims of the scientists is to find forage plants for the flocks and herds. One way they think the pastures might be extended is by sowing seeds from aircraft. Like Taylor, the Controller of Agriculture in Tripolitania, who has the same idea about trees, they see the possibilities of dropping seeds in capsules. The tiny seed-pills would contain enough food and drink to enable the seeds to survive and take root in the arid regions.

Iraq is already the biggest cattle-rearing country in the Middle East and the experts dream of making it a second Texas, with the possibility of a large export trade in meat. The country already has flocks totalling 12,000,000 sheep and it is reckoned that that can at least be doubled. They are breeding special varieties of cattle and sheep, adapted to the conditions of the country and to the needs of the country. For example, they want to improve the Southern Arabi sheep and produce a fine wool for weaving.

Iraq grows over 30,000,000 date palms, a third of the world's total, and second in importance only to the date is rice, in the marshlands of the south.

One of the problems of Iraq is that it is under-populated. For intensive cultivation it would need a much larger population than the 5,000,000 which is the present estimate ('estimate', because here again the desert tribes have a strong reluctance to being counted and invariably forget to include their wives in any census.) Some of the experts consider that if Iraq could use fully modern agricultural equipment and methods, with its own oil available, it could develop a prosperous agriculture, even with a limited population, and become a big exporting country.

It is certainly capable of feeding many times more people than it does today, and does only on a very low standard. In the days of the Caliphate of Haroun Al Raschid and the Arabian Nights, it is reckoned that Mesopotamia sustained a population of between 30 million and 40 million, and that Baghdad itself had a population of 2,000,000. It certainly had 30,000 public baths!

# CHAPTER NINE

## PERSIAN CARPET — OF SALT

ROBIN, aged four, was unimpressed either by history or by the snow-clad peaks over which he was flying. He was just miserable. It was his first flight and on the airport he had been hopping with impatience and excitement, and now they were being unkind to him. They were trying to fit a face mask on him and Robin had just had his tonsils out and had had an anaesthetic, and he had not liked the anaesthetic. Nobody could persuade him that oxygen was not just that nasty stuff he had had in hospital.

He was surrounded by masked faces, including those of his father and mother, and he did not like that either. When the steward tried to coax him, he just struggled and yelled, and the more he wrestled, the bluer he became. At the great height at which we had to fly, he was wasting what little oxygen there was in the cabin. Then he became exhausted and curled up sleepily with the mask beside him, leaking enough oxygen to keep him going.

A modern airliner travels only 2½ hours to get from Baghdad to Teheran. In less time than it takes to go from London to Birmingham by rail, one crosses the great barrier range of the Zagros, which was the watershed not only of great rivers but of great cultures. One vaults over the perilous passes through which the Aryan races and ultimately the Mongols descended upon the west, and through which Alexander the Great's armies marched eastwards to India.

We crossed the 'Hump' at 17,000 feet, because the weather was treacherous and there were dangerous peaks to negotiate before we emerged into the High Plateau of Persia itself. As we approached Teheran, which is itself 3,000 ft. above sea level, the great range of the Elburz, which separates the interior of Persia from the Caspian, rose up ahead and with it the mountain pyramid of Mount Damavand, 19,000 ft. high, and covered with snow.

I was much less interested, however, in the mountain panorama than in the landscape below, because it revealed something about which I had not been forewarned, and something which no one in the aircraft, not even the pilot who had made the flight scores of times, could explain.

The first startling impression of the approaches to Teheran is that there has been a heavy bombing—not of the capital itself but of the countryside, for thousands of square miles around. Pock-marks of craters pit the landscape with an extravagance which I had not seen except on the bombed battle-fields of Western Europe. It looks like 'pattern bombing' but of an extraordinary kind. The craters are in regular lines suggesting the results of sticks of bombs, but they criss-cross and interlace.

Almost my first question, after I had wrestled with the inevitable customs, currency and passport difficulties, was about these craters. It took me some time to get any clue, because those who live in Persia and take *qanats* completely for granted, could not recognise them from my aerial description of them. I have since found that most of the literature on Persia is equally off-hand about *qanats*, although, or perhaps because, they are such a familiar feature of Persia.

Curiosity about these *qanats* was to take me ranging not only across the countryside but far into history, because these *qanats* are supposed to date back about 5,000 years.

*Qanats* are horizontal wells, or underground channels, with vertical shafts—those craters which so impressed me. The shafts are at intervals of about 50 yards and, in the construction of *qanats,* are used to remove the waste excavated by the miners. They can serve as ventilating shafts and as wells. The *qanat* diggers go down to the bedrock of an underground stream and drive galleries along the incline of the water-bearing layer. To keep their bearings underground they use a primitive form of magnetic compass. This practice is so old that some Persians claim that the compass must have originated here. This claim is also made by the Chinese and the Arabs. In China the lodestone, or a piece of iron which has been touched by the lodestone, making it direct itself to the magnetic north, is said to have been used in the 3rd century B.C. The Arabs were using the compass in the Eastern Mediterranean in the 13th century A.D. Whether or not the Persians discovered it independently, or borrowed it from the East, it is perfectly plausible that the compass reached the Mediterranean via Persia.

Horizontally these *qanats* can be of considerable length. The longest known is near Yezd and stretches underground for 30 miles. Vertically the deepest, at Gunabad, in Eastern Persia, is 1,000 ft. The average depth is about 60 ft. and the average length about five miles. There are over 50,000 *qanats* in Persia with a capacity varying from half a cubic foot to 5 cubic ft. a second. However remote their origin may really be, some around Persepolis are known to be 2,000 years old.

These *qanats* may be commonplace to the Persians who have used them so long, but they are fascinating to scientists. Balliol College, Oxford, sent out in the summer of 1950 an expedition to explore the *qanats* of Kerman in the heart of Persia, because of the possibility that locked in them were unique forms of Nature.

The theory is that the great convulsion which threw up the Central Plain of Persia, folded the rim of mountains round it, separated the Caspian Sea from the Persian Gulf, and created the oil "domes" which are the wealth of Persia, may have trapped primitive forms of life in these underground river beds. There is, for instance, the belief in the existence of blind white fish of a type unknown elsewhere today. Existing with it there must be the primitive forms on which it feeds.

I, too, wanted to do some subterranean exploration of the *qanats,* but circumstances were unpropitious. I went out to trace the course of the *qanats* which start in the mountains above Gulhek, the mountain village north of Teheran, where the British Embassy goes in summer. Unfortunately, a

workman fell down one of the shafts. It was 150 ft. deep, but
he escaped with a broken leg, and a rescue party was lowered
by a wooden winch down one of the vertical shafts. They
carried him up the incline of the water-course about half-a-
mile to another shaft, through which they hoisted him. The
accident and the fact that the *qanat* was then in spate
discouraged me from the venture.

These *qanats* are usually a joint enterprise between two
sets of landlords—the owners of the high but poor land and
the owners many miles away of good land in need of water.
Usually they take the precaution of marrying into each other's
family. In partnership they create these freshwater drains.

When the *qanats* emerge into open channels, they distri-
bute the water into *jubes,* wide gutters, which supply villages
and towns, including Teheran, the capital. These *jubes* run
uncovered through the main streets of Teheran and can, as I
found, be extremely treacherous on a dark night. From these
the people collect their drinking and washing water, but one
would be foolhardy to drink it unboiled by the time it crosses
a town. Certainly I would not drink water like that in which
I tripped.

Drinking water in Teheran is called 'British Embassy',
because the only purification system is in the Embassy
grounds and the 'safe' water for hotels and private houses is
bought and sold by water carriers.

These open gullies and the fouling of the water which is
bound to happen are strange in the country of Zoroaster,
whose third principle was that *The elements—air, fire, water
and earth—are pure and must not be defiled.* It is true that
Zoroastrians are now a tiny minority in a country where the
principal religion is Islam, but the influence of Zoroaster is
still implicit. He was the Prophet of Iran, born it is believed,
in the 7th century B.C. His other two basic principles were
*Agriculture and cattle breeding are the only noble callings*
and *The whole of creation is a combat between good and evil.*
One of the features of Zoroastrianism is the profound
reverence for fire, so that Zoroastrians have come to be called

Fire Worshippers. This is a justifiable superstition in a country where fire springs out of the ground. The origins of the great oil industry of Persia can be attributed to fire worship, since the discovery of the great oilfields on the Persian Gulf was due to a natural undying fire sanctified by the priests of Zoroaster—a few miles north of Abadan where the oil comes to the surface.

Getting out into the deserts of Teheran was not as casual as hiring a taxi to go through the Wilderness of Sinai. The expedition which I joined was a convoy of specially-equipped trucks. For over two months the administrators of the Seven Year Plan had been preparing the details and the provisions for this expedition of Swiss geologists. It was going into places where men had possibly never penetrated before, into a part of the range of mountains of Persian Baluchistan, off the tracks of the Indo-Aryan migrations and of modern communications. It was to take the geologists across the Great Salt Lake Desert of the north and the not-so-salt Lout, the sand desert of the south. They might as well have been going to spend the

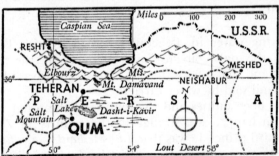

season in the Antarctic, since they had to be completely self-sufficient. Three large, balloon-tyred trucks, and two jeeps, with their driver-fitters, were needed for a party of four geologists—Professor Heim, Dr. K. T. Goldschmid, Dr. Huber and Dr. Stocklin, and Mrs. Heim who was going along as housekeeper for the party. They were led out into the desert by the Persian Geological Director, Dr. B. Mostofi, who was escorting them in the south and returning to organise a similar expedition to the north. I was going part of the way with them, through the *Dasht-i-Kavir*, the Great Salt Desert.

When we entered the Great Salt Desert, Dr. Goldschmid, with whom I was sharing a truck, became as excited as a small boy on his first visit to the cinema. He was thrilled; he was enraptured; he was ecstatic. Every now and again he would make the driver hoot a warning that we were breaking convoy, a warning which is necessary in these remote places, where every member of the convoy makes himself responsible for the rest. He would stop the truck and run up a hill to take a photograph. The whole convoy would halt while he and his colleagues scrambled over the rocks, with their geological hammers, chipping pieces and examining them under magnifying glasses. Like Boy Scouts discovering a spoor, they would shout and whistle to each other and cluster around to compare some fossilised imprint of a prehistoric animal, relic of the days before this great plateau was thrust up from the bottom of the sea.

Goldschmid, with a lifetime of geological surveys behind him, made no effort to conceal his excitement. After all my weeks of desert landscapes, I would look around a desolate view and concede that it was 'pretty good'.

'Pretty good!' he would protest indignantly, 'it's beautiful!'

The adjective, applied to that stark barrenness, might seem misplaced, but allowance had to be made for the fact that he was seeing it with the eyes of a geologist—of a scientific prospector whose life up till then had been spent in the tropical jungles of Central and South America. There the geological formations are densely clothed by vegetation. Here they were stripped naked, scoured of soil and riven and rent, until every seam and vein was visible. He was like a biologist who might ignore a glamorous film-star and rave about a microscopic section of cell-tissues.

I must confess that even I, who had learned almost to satiation that deserts so far from being monotonous can have infinite variety, was moved to adjectives myself when we first looked down on the great salt lake. The sun was on it and it was all shimmering white with heat veils swirling above it. In the background were the snow-clad mountains of the Elburz and on the unbroken horizon to the east, a mirage with a detail such as I have never seen—and I had seen plenty over the sand deserts. This was a salt-mirage.

A mirage is an optical illusion common in the hot deserts. The sand, or in this case, the salt, being heated by the sun causes the surrounding air to expand and alters the refractive index. Any object seen across such a heated area is made visible by two sets of rays, bent by the different densities of the atmosphere. The image of the sky is turned upside down by the reflection from the salt (or sand) and is all mixed up with other reflections of objects beyond the horizon. The mirage suspended over the salt lake created the image of a great blue sea with tropical islands and lagoons—and a camel, the ship of the desert, looks a strange craft.

Presently we saw ahead of us what might have been an even more spectacular mirage but which materialised as the Holy City of Qum. This city of the Salt Desert has an incredible skyline of domes and slender minarets. In the middle, dazzling by its brilliance, was the dome of the Mosque of Fatima, which is encased in solid gold an eighth-of-an-inch thick, and framed in minarets of coloured porcelain. It seemed almost as though there were two suns in the sky.

Qum is a beautiful but unfriendly city for strangers and before we entered it Dr. Mostofi stopped the convoy for a 'briefing'. He warned us that we would have to be very cautious in our behaviour and above all to keep cameras out of sight. The people of the city are devout Moslems of a very strict sect, who may tolerate the presence of Infidels but not their practices. Cameras, the 'makers of images', are an abomination, so much so that when I tried both here and later back in Teheran to get photographs of the Mosque of Fatima, I could only get drawings. We were not allowed anywhere near the mosque and were threatened by a *mullah,* or priest, when we dawdled for a moment on a bridge above a stream where women, heavily veiled, were washing clothes. It is almost inviting a riot even to glance at the harems, the women's quarters, where, behind grilles curtained by heavy carpets, their Lords-and-Masters hide their females.

West of Qum is one of the highest of the many mountains of salt in the Salt Desert. This 'plug' rises 3,000 ft. above the plateau, which itself is 3,000 ft. high and is jammed between two ridges of mountains. The upheaval which at the end of the Pliocene Age 600,000 years ago wrinkled the earth's crust to form these mountains, used these mountains to squeeze up this salt formation like a jerk of toothpaste.

Long before we got to the Salt Mountain we could see long trains of camels coming out of the passes and across the desert, converging on and diverging from the salt plug. We passed returning camels with slabs of rock salt as big as tombstones slung across their humps. Our trail lay over crunching salt plains and across rivers of salt until it brought us to a caravan-serai at the foot of the mountains—a large mud-wall compound for the camels and open verandahs for the camel drivers to sleep in. High up on a ridge of salt we could see the dwarfed figure of the look-out of the salt-mine. He watched us climb up the narrow pass, which camels took more sure-footedly than I did, and then with a shout to his fellows hidden in the recesses of the mountains, he came bounding down the slopes to meet us as the seneschal of the Crystal Fortress. He greeted us with friendly *salaams* and led us through a cleft in the mountains.

This was a most uncomfortable experience because we were jostled by camels, snorting and sneering in their usual fashion, slavering their frothy mouths menacingly at us (and a bite from the septic mouth of a camel is particularly nasty) and lurching their salty loads in a way that threatened to crush us against the rocks. The breath, or rather the belch, of a camel is so foul that even recalling it makes me feel sick. Every now and again one of them, like a small boy blowing bubble-gum, would blow out of the side of its mouth a fleshy balloon. This is a swelling of the *uvula* (that wobbly protuberance which dangles in the throat) and is accompanied by a loud gurgling noise, like the bathwater running out. When camels are 'blowing bubbles' it is wise to give them a wide berth and in this narrow, salt crevasse, there was no wide berth to give them.

As we climbed there was a growing hubbub from what seemed to be the inside of the mountains. It sounded as though there were a terrific quarrel going on. There was a hubbub of voices, yells and rumbles. As the rocks narrowed above us, I thought we were burrowing into the heart of the mountain, but presently we emerged, not into a mine, but into a quarry, open to the sky. What had sounded like a terrific quarrel was just the cheerful workaday shouts of the miners and the drivers having their usual arguments with the camels.

The rocks of the quarry looked like white marble, which the *gaffeer* or "gaffer" licked to prove it was not. Suddenly, he grabbed me by the arm and, in Persian (which I did not understand) started to hustle me out of the quarry. I wanted to stay but there was a great commotion and the drivers belaboured and kicked the huddle of kneeling camels to their feet, hounded them out of the quarry and up the mountainside. There was no further argument. I was swept upwards in the surge.

It was just as well, because we had scarcely got clear before there was a dynamite explosion and great slabs of salt went crashing down. With a cheer, the miners, like dusky gnomes, went swarming back into the pit and started splitting the rocks and loading them on to the camels.

The *gaffeer* took me up to the watchtower ledge and pointed out the great white sweep of the salt-encrusted valley. The camel drivers who joined us tried to 'pull my leg' by gestures which were meant to convey that it was snow. They scooped up imaginary handfuls and rolled them into imaginary snowballs and had an imaginary battle until the *gaffeer* very solemnly reproved them for trying to deceive an innocent stranger, and equally solemnly they bowed and gestured apologetically.

By the time we got out of the recesses of the salt mountains the sun was setting and we started off across the Salt Desert in the gathering dusk.

The Central Deserts cover more than half of Persia, with more than two-thirds of them salt-poisoned beyond, I suspect, any hope of recovery. This, in a sense, is the price which the country pays for its oil wealth. The impervious clay which underlies it is the 'tarpaulin' which has kept the oil from escaping to the surface and imprisoned it for millions of years. But the same clay also excludes the possibilities of underground water, because it prevents water from seeping into the spongy rocks. Borings over 8,000 ft. deep have not touched water.

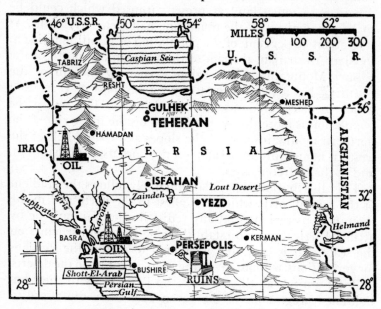

So the plateau is a clay-lined basin into which the surrounding hills pour their water. The water dissolves out the salt from the rocks and, as it evaporates, spreads an ever-increasing layer of salt. Incidentally, I was told that the word *Lout*, as applied to the Southern Desert, is a Persian form of *Lot* and harks back to the same origins as the Biblical story when Lot's wife was turned into a pillar of salt. This is just another example of the close inter-relation of all the Middle Eastern countries and of their common folklores.

If salt were an economic proposition, Persia would possess

in it greater wealth than is represented even by its oil. The salt mountain which I visited could supply the whole population of China, which is short of salt, with all it requires for centuries. All that the salt does at the moment is to destroy the fertility of half the country.

In discussions which I had with the Faculties of the University of Teheran and with the experts of the Seven Year Plan, they argued not unreasonably that Persia at present, and for many years to come, could afford to ignore the Central Deserts. There is so much land at present unused which could be made productive that the remaining half seems irrelevant. As it is, about 50 per cent. of the population of 12 millions live in Persian Azerbaijan, the rim of the Caspian Sea north of the Elburz Mountains. This region—a narrow margin of the country—has a heavy rainfall and a lushness of vegetation which in places amounts to tropical jungle. The rest of the population is more thinly distributed on the inner rim of the northern mountains and on the slopes and coastal belt of the western mountains, in Seistan, on the borders of Afghanistan, and in the scattered oases.

This distribution of population largely follows the gradient of the rainfall map, which is highest in the north and in the mountainous regions, and any redistribution can only be by artificial irrigation. To establish these irrigation schemes on the scale that is projected is enough to occupy the Persians for generations, without diverting their attention to the deserts.

But I am not at all sure that the Persians, with their enlightened programme of the Seven Year Plan, can afford to disregard the deserts.

The Persian scientists with whom I discussed this listened most politely to the unasked advice of a stranger. At one session I quoted Omar Khayyam and was surprised to find how little response the name produced until one professor explained to me that few intellectuals in Persia took any account of Omar as a poet. They would have recognised him if I had discussed him as an astronomer and philosopher, but as a poet, no! He does not rank, in their opinion, in the same category as, for example, Firdousi, Rudagi or Fakhr-ad-Din

As'ad, or Ansari. In fact, a Persian graduate from Cambridge said that as a poet Omar Khayyam, in the original Persian, was vastly inferior to Fitzgerald who, in translating him into English, made him a better poet than he was.

Nevertheless, I quoted him (or Fitzgerald):

'They say the Lion and the Lizard keep
The Courts where Jamshyd gloried and drank deep;
And Bahram, that great Hunter—the Wild Ass
Stamps o'er his head, and he lies fast asleep'.

That, I said, sounded to me like invasion by the desert and, please, could they tell me what had happened to the Courts of Jamshyd and Bahram?

Jamshyd is a legendary king, who is supposed to have founded Persepolis, that great ruined city which stands north of Shiraz in a high plain which is planned as one of the development areas. But Bahram was even more illuminating, for his capital was Nishapur. Nishapur was the birthplace of Omar Khayyam, which in his day (11th century), or certainly a century later at the time of Gengis Khan, was a great oasis with a population of a million-and-a-half. Today it can sustain only 15,000 people. Wars had a lot to do with that, but so had the extension of desert conditions.

A desert is never stationary. It is always on the move. Wherever man's grip on the soil slackens and his defences break down, the desert moves in—the counter-offensive of the desert itself. In the deserts of Persia and on their edges are oases and fertile stretches which are menaced by wind-drift of salt and sand and by the erosion of wind and water. In the area of Khorasan there was, in ancient times, a great forest of which not a vestige is left today. Kerman and the stretches of the Lout south to Baluchistan must, in Alexander the Great's time, have been a relatively fertile area where now there is not a single village or hamlet, nothing but desert. Yet there in the Bampur Valley Alexander sustained his army for two months. And there are plenty of other instances of desert encroachment.

Water figures large in the Seven Year Plan for the regeneration of Persia. Of the £200 millions, ranging from education and health to afforestation and mining, 23 per cent. has been earmarked for irrigation and agriculture.

Water, after oil, is Persia's biggest export. From the high mountain rim, Persia sends 66 per cent. of its total rainfall into rivers which flow into other countries. A sovereign state has the right to do what it likes with the water within its frontiers and certainly Persia could divert to its own uses a very large part of the water which now spills into other states. But it also raises very important international issues. Curiously enough Persia has become involved in an international dispute over water—not water that it is withholding from someone else, but water which Afghanistan withheld from it. The only substantial amount of water which Persia 'imports' is a river which runs from Afghanistan into Persian Seistan. Some years ago, in a period of water shortage, the Afghans dammed the river and cut off its flow into Seistan, with the result that at least 3,000 people died of starvation. Persia, in its planning, therefore, is aware of its responsibility as a major watershed.

The Seven Year Plan, which is led by Prince Abdul Reza, the younger brother of the Shah, is administered by Dr. M. Naficy, a remarkable character by any standards, and is 'processed' by Overseas Consultants Inc. This is mainly American but it enlisted, for irrigation, Mr. Henry Olivier, a British hydrologist.

One of the first difficulties of the plan was to get figures. This is an example of the extraordinary contradiction which is Persia—a country of long history and tradition and of a high intellectual culture, but technologically and socially extremely backward. It is this backwardness which this ambitious plan of social and economic reorganisation is designed to remove in seven annual stages. It is, in effect, a ploughing back into the soil and social life of Persia the wealth which is beneath that soil in the form of oil. All that is known about population figures is that there may be between 12,000,000 and 15,000,000 people in this country which has an area of 628,000 square miles. The population, everyone admits, has a low standard of life.

There is practically no irrigation in Persia, but, under the plan, it is reckoned that areas known to be fertile but arid could support seven persons for every two acres. So, accepting the Central Deserts as hopeless for the time being, the accessible fertile areas which form at least a fifth of Persia could, with mechanised agriculture, support and feed many millions more. They could raise very greatly the standard of life of the existing population and probably put Persia in a position to export food to its hungry neighbours, the teeming populations of the Indian sub-continent.

There are many schemes, but only one has been really got under way. This is designed to take some of the headwaters of the Karoun River and direct the water into the desert bowl around the big and ancient city of Isfahan. The Karoun is the big river which joins the Tigris and the Euphrates in Iraq and becomes the Shott-El-Arab, but in its early stages it runs almost parallel to the Zaindeh Rud, which waters the great oasis of Isfahan.

The rivers are separated by a range of mountains through which a tunnel is being driven to increase the flow of the Zaindeh Rud and, in addition to supplying the considerable industrial needs of Isfahan, will bring at least 60,000 more acres into cultivation. This scheme was first thought of 350 years ago.

Marching together with the plans for irrigation are enlightened afforestation schemes. The Persian Government enlisted the help of a remarkable British forestry expert, Mr. V. K. Maitland.

'Vic', who died tragically a few weeks after my visit while on an expedition in the northern mountains, was a real 'man against the desert'—only he would be very indignant at being described as such because he maintained that he was not 'against the desert'. Men, he argued, could achieve nothing *against* the desert, but only in complete co-operation *with* it. This energetic, wiry, little man, who might have passed unnoticed in a suburban railway train, had traversed the deserts

K

of India, Pakistan, Afghanistan, Persia, Iraq and the whole of North Africa, and had left his imprint on practically every scheme for the recovery of those areas.

His gospel was the gospel of trees. I recall him lamenting to me in Whitehall—he was expert adviser to the Foreign Office —that everyone thought he was crazy when he spoke of planting trees in the desert. No one could see the relation of forest and desert, and yet the story of deserts (as I found) is to a great extent the story of vanished forests. It was Maitland's job, under the Seven Year Plan, to try to restore the forests and clothe again with trees the mountain rim of the Central Deserts.

With a sweep of his arm towards the snow-clad mountains of the Elburz, he said 'See that snow. In a few weeks it will thaw. As water it will pour off the mountains, rush down in spate and lose itself in the desert. But if there were trees, the trees would hold that snow for months and it would melt gradually, seep into the ground, feed into the rivers on a proper rationing system, and spread the supply of water far into the dry season.'

And so the Persians who, in ancient times, gave us the *qanats* and the windmills, and methods of supplying and conserving water, are re-thinking their history and trying to make themselves again the masters of the waters which can make this largely arid country lush and fertile, not just a granary but an orchard.

They do not agree, nowadays, with Omar Khayyam that 'Wilderness is Paradise enow' even with 'a loaf of bread, a flask of wine, a book of verse—and thou.'

# CHAPTER TEN

# ONE MORE RIVER TO CROSS

BEERSHEBA is a frontier town—not in terms of the map, though, because actually it is in the centre of the modern State of Israel. It is a 'frontier town' because beyond lies the desert of the Negev, the barren land which is the challenge to the Jewish settlers.

An Israeli scribe did not like my newspaper description of Beersheba as *The Wild West in an Eastern setting,* but I do not think he could have ever been there, because there, with modern variations, is all the bustle and excitement, the sense of adventure which we associate with the pioneer days of the Santa Fe and the Oregon Trail. You have to leave out the saloons and the dancing girls, because they are no part of this purposeful town, and you have to substitute jeeps for bronchos and trucks for covered-wagons. But you have the

mechanised sheriffs' *posses* riding in from their patrols. You find the pioneers with their children—Jews from all over the world—arriving to 'stake out their claims.' Around the corner you find the equivalent of theMarshal's Office, with the maps of the Negev displaying all the unborn colonies. When you propose going south from Beersheba, the Army insists on giving you a rifle or a revolver with the injunction 'Shoot it out'. Being a harmless sort of a chap who has never wanted to 'shoot it out' with anyone, I made my excuses, but was told very firmly that my life was in my own hands. And that I was going into the Bad Lands where marauders shoot first and do not ask or wait for explanations.

This was not pure melodrama. We were going out into the desert tracts which are the favourite crossing route of Arab infiltrators, mainly armed bands running contraband, in time-honoured fashion, from Asia to Africa, with the added excuse of the Jewish-Arab 'troubles'. These raiders regard travellers and the Jewish settlers as legitimate prey and attack the isolated settlements, killing the settlers and carrying off their stocks.

Around Beersheba are forty settlements, most of them recent. They are farmed by former shock-troopers, including young girls, who, with their rifles within reach, till the fields which they have wrested from the sands. As the farmers put up their frame-houses, lay pipelines and ride tractors, they keep a vigilant eye on the horizon for the sudden swoop of camel-raiders.

We stowed the rifles and ammunition in the back of the jeep and set off into the thirstlands, which stretch to the Gulf of Akaba 120 miles beyond Beersheba. For part of the way the road was good. Indeed, with the Jewish passion for trees, it was being turned into an avenue. It was indeed a remarkable sight, in that arid desolation, to see men many miles from anywhere planting trees by the roadside and watering them, as they have to do continuously, from water carts. That is part of the duty of the newly established settlements, who make themselves responsible for the nearest stretch of road, and they will haul water for miles to give the young saplings a drink until their roots can go down to find water for themselves. It is an impressive act of faith by which a generation, which has still to find the necessities for its own survival, is planting trees for future generations.

In these new settlements, the desert is coming to life. The rainfall is virtually non-existent, but, defying climate, they are cultivating the good earth.

At Revivim, one of the southernmost outposts, I had the memorable experience of wading knee-deep in lucerne grass, which was yielding three crops a year from soil which only a few years before had been meaningless desert and, in the interval, had been a battlefield. Here, too, for the first time, I heard birds singing in the desert and saw brilliantly coloured butterflies fluttering among man-planted flowers. How did these butterflies get there? I had seen desert butterflies, moths with a sand-coloured 'camouflage' adapted to their surroundings; but these butterflies at Revivim—miles from any garden —had changed their costume to match the flowers. The air was scent-laden and the bees were swarming—the black, wild bees which, after scrounging a living from the desert, had discovered a banquet.

There was milk as well as honey in this part which was not the Promised Land but the Wilderness of Zin. A fine herd of pedigree cows, a recent gift from America, to replace the cattle destroyed during the bombardment of the colonists at Revivim, was feeding on the lucerne harvest and on root crops grown in the desert. When man 'shows willing', Nature is always ready to lend a hand. There was a remarkable crop of wild clover. No one knows where it came from. Somehow Nature had been hoarding this, just waiting for water.

Revivim in Hebrew means *Drops of Water*. That, in terms of rain, is about all it amounts to. But nearby is the Wadhi Asluig, which comes down from the bare hills. When a storm breaks, the water comes down as a wall of water sometimes as high as 18 ft. Just before my visit, the spate had brought destruction with it. The colonists had constructed a concrete catchment dam and the floods had washed out a landmine somewhere in the old battlefield and had swept it down to blow up the dam. But even this could not discourage the colonists.

By a system of diversion dams, carrying the water into channels 1,000 yards long, they have brought the water into the fields and into the reservoir which stores 80,000 cubic metres of water. This storage is only incidental, because they have an intelligent way of farming by which the spate is allowed to flush a series of sloping machine-graded fields, large shallow terraces. The water floods over the first terrace, spills into the second and finishes up in the third. Immediately the flooding takes place, the settlers move in and plough to let the water down into the subsoil. They immediately plant the crops but they plant only the amount of ground which has been flooded. They do not count on a second spate. If it comes it is just a bonus.

There is a well at Revivim drawing water from a depth of 300 ft., but it is salty. They overcome this by diluting it in the reservoir with the floodwaters of the *wadhi* and use it for canalised irrigation of the olive and citrus groves.

During the Arab-Jewish war, Revivim was entirely cut off and surrounded by Egyptian forces, but it held out for months and was never taken. During the siege the colonists had to 'dig in' and in the course of excavating a shelter, they uncovered a ready-made dug-out—a pillared cave which was probably a Byzantine water-tank. Strange that two sets of colonists so far removed in time should have chosen the identical site.

Or is it? Ten miles away across the desert are the ruins of the Byzantine city of Subetta. To find it we had to go by a compass bearing.

At this stage Mr. O. Goldslager, the Director of Soil Conservation of the State of Israel, who was the escort, firmly insisted that we buckle on our cartridge belts, load our rifles and hold them at 'the ready', because we were now deep in the danger zone. In the bumping ride across desert where there was not even a track, I was more scared of my loaded rifle than I was of the possible marauders.

The ruined city of Subetta has been only partly excavated, but what has been revealed is evidence of a considerable and prosperous city and the profile of the neighbourhood shows it must have been an extensive community. There are at least three Byzantine churches of a scale and impressiveness which suggest that this was not just a 'good pull-up for camels' or a whistle-halt on a desert trail. The reconstructed villas are proof of a culture and a prosperity in an area which is now inhospitable—or appears to be so.

There is, for instance, in one of the basilicas, a baptismal font, for total immersion—significant in a spot which has less than four inches of rainfall. 'This', some of the experts may say, 'is proof that in the last two thousand years the climate and the rainfall must have changed'; but the surrounding countryside disproves this. We saw what had now become, to me, the familiar lay-out of the water-traps—terraces now submerged in dust and the ancient wells and cisterns—and the extraordinary apparition of the dew-mounds.

It would have been worth travelling a long way just to see these. Not that a pile of pebbles is of itself very exciting, but the meaning is profoundly significant. In this area around Subetta the entire landscape is covered with 'pimples', a regular rash. And I mean 'regular', because the mounds are arranged in geometrical rows, or in some cases stretch out as dykes. At first sight one might imagine that in olden times some conscientious farmers must have done a very thorough job of clearing their land of stones and had tidily piled them up at intervals. That, however, is not the meaning of the mounds.

When we went to explore them, on foot, the escort insisted sternly that we take our rifles, because we were going into the hills, through the defiles of which the marauders make their surprise attacks.

The mounds are about a metre high and are now choked in dust. But, in the past, the pebble traps were kept clear of dust. They were there to trap the dew. They were a device to exploit the extremes of heat and cold. The cold pebbles in the morning condensed the moisture out of the atmosphere, and it seeped through the pile of pebbles into the good earth below. In these mounds were planted fig trees and olives and there is some evidence of even bigger trees. But, in any event, the desert by this device was turned into groves.

These dew mounds are supposed to be much older than the Byzantine Age, and to go back perhaps some 3,000 years, which would make them coincide with the period of the Nabateans, who were mentioned in the chapter on Sinai. Certainly a culture which was capable of hewing a city out of rocks, as they did at Petra, was capable also of the ingenuity shown in these mounds.

The Israeli scientists have given considerable attention to dew. For them the Bible is a valuable (though not infallible) source-book of scientific information and dew receives a good deal of attention in the Old Testament—in an era consistent with these dew mounds. Even *manna* is connected with dew. The little tamarisk-louse *Mannafera aphis* depends on dew as much as on the leaves on which it feeds. The *manna* is 'delivered' in the dawn at the time of dew condensation.

One of the leading experts is Dr. S. Duvdevani, of the Agricultural School at Pardes Hanna (The Orange Grove of Hannah). He has perfected 'dew meters', by which exact measurements can be made of dew content in the atmosphere, and has made possible a careful study of the phenomenon of dew. Some of the results are surprising. Anyone who has endured *khamsin*—the hot, blistering wind of the desert—will assure you emphatically that it is unbearably 'dry'. Yet the measurements have shown that this 'dry' wind contains moisture equivalent to that in the atmosphere after rain and the greatest concentration of dew is at a metre from the ground, the height of the ancient dew mounds! What modern scientific methods can tell us with precision merely confirms the skills and the intelligence of the Ancients.

Ground travel through the Negev can teach one a lot about the nature and variety of the desert, and about what can be done with it when people have courage and enterprise to plant the wilderness as the communal settlers have done. I wanted, however, to get a more comprehensive idea of what the Negev 'added up to'. So I flew over it, in a freight plane carrying a cargo of cement.

The Negev seen from 5,000 ft. would justify those who dismiss the desert as 'hopeless'. One looks down on the great

ᴇʀᴛ ᴘɪ ᴘᴇ-
ᴇ: Water
carried a
dred miles
the Bibli-
Wilderness.

ᴇ ʀᴇsᴜʟᴛ:
ee deep in
erne grass
aree crops a
.

MYSTERY-MOISTURE: How plants and sand beetles survive in dry dunes. Pierre, ecologist, against background of Saharan mud fort seeks insects which give clue to hidden moisture.

—AND DRY MOUNDS which may be the answer. Biblical Wilderness 3,000 years ago Ancients trapped dew with help of pebbles. (Author's desert cap.)

clefts and ravines, on a landscape gashed by water and wind erosion with great sand tracts and dry *wadhis*, with scarcely any visible vegetation to encourage the prospect of more. To the east, between the Dead Sea and the Gulf of Akaba, is the desert valley of Arabah. On the west are the limestone ranges of the Tih, flat-topped. On the east is a low gap in the hills with three peaks visible beyond. This is the Wadhi Itham, which turns the eastern range of the Arabah, and through which the Israelites passed on their way to Moab on the eastern side of the Jordan. In the background is Mount Hor, at the base of which is the ancient city of Petra. The Arabah is a dividing line between Israel and Jordan and the brilliantly coloured mountains are on the Jordan side. At high noon they have a sunset glow.

We landed at Elatt, the Jewish garrison post at the head of the Gulf of Akaba. Here the triangle of the Israelite Negev comes to a narrow point. Four miles to the east is the Jordan seaport. Five miles to the west is the Egyptian settlement of Taba, and facing us was the Hedjaz—four countries with a foothold on a narrow neck of water.

On their foothold the Jews were creating, not only a garrison base, but a seaside resort. Out of the dunes they were constructing a park to attract the visitors and a hotel of comfortable mud bungalows. When they took over, all the water had to be carried across the desert from the nearest Israel outposts south of Beersheba, but they set out industriously boring for water. They sank wells and got only salt water. They also found wells which had been there in ancient times but which had gone salty. Then, ten miles away, they struck sweet water and are piping it into the settlement. To make the most of the fishing in the Gulf, they carried boats across the desert. The Suez Canal was closed to them and the only way to reach Akaba by sea from Mediterranean Palestine would have been a complete circumnavigation of the continent of Africa.

The Negev is the great challenge to Israel. This desert forms more than half its territory. One rarely finds it even shown in the former maps of Palestine, the limits of which were the Biblical 'from Dan to Beersheba'. Israeli scientists assured me that one day the Negev would be as productive as those areas which I saw with rich cultivation in the north—areas which, when the first settlers of Zion moved in 80 years ago, were hopeless malarial marshes.

It will take all the scientific ingenuity which Israel can command to achieve this object, but the problems are being tackled with imagination. At the Weizmann Institute, at Rehovot, chemists, physicists and soil experts are carrying out experiments to provide the ultra-modern answers.

I saw a solar distillation plant which daily produces 40 litres of pure water from heavily salted water. It is a glass frame shaped like a prism, orientated to the sun's maximum intensity. The angle of the inclined side of the prism is important. It concentrates the heat of the sun on the water and evaporates it, to condense on the colder vertical glass at the back, from which it drips into gutters.

The answer to the needs of settlers afflicted with a brackish soil or salted water is more likely to be the ion-exchange plant which I saw operating at the Institute. This consists of tubes charged with resins, specially produced by the President of Israel, Dr. Chaim Weizmann, the world-famous chemist. The salt water parts with its sodium in one tube; in the next the acid is removed; and in the course of a day it can produce ten tons of water, with the salt water content reduced to any degree necessary. This was about to be sent off as a foolproof plant to one of the settlements.

Even more imaginative is the proposal to use nylon. If we think of nylon as expensive stockings, this sounds absurd. That is not the way the Israeli scientists think of it. They are experimenting with sheet nylon as a means of extracting fresh water from salt sources and from the brackish soil. There are various ways in which it can be done. Nylon allows the heat rays of the sun to get through but its surface remains cold. Therefore, the water steams off through the nylon and condenses on the cold surface. If nylon is spread over running salt water or soil which is moist, though bitter, the moisture will be distilled off and can be captured. One way is to have fields covered with nylon furrows. The distilled water runs into the trough of the furrow and can be collected; or the furrows can be filled with good soil and you could have crops on an exaggerated window-box principle.

Nylon, however, has another characteristic of which they want to make use. One of the biggest problems of the desert is the evaporation of water from open reservoirs (the reservoir at Revivim loses two inches of water from its surface per week; that, over its area, is a lot of precious water). The scientists have the idea of covering these open reservoirs with nylon flakes. Flake-nylon, unlike sheet-nylon, is opaque and not translucent; it keeps out light, and in this case heat, whereas the clear nylon passes both. If, say the scientists, the reservoirs are covered with nylon flakes (like soap flakes in appearance) they will float and rise and fall with the water, and will reflect back all the heat waves of the sun and prevent the water underneath from steaming off.

This sort of thing is entirely feasible to scientists who were capable of the ingenious tricks for getting minerals out of the Dead Sea. There, at the shallow end, where the water covers what was once Sodom and Gomorrah, are the salt pans—huge shallow trays where the Dead Sea water is evaporated by the sun and leaves the wealth of its minerals as a crust. To speed up the process of steaming off the water, the scientists decided to lend the sun a hand. They wanted to use more of its heat rays. Some colours absorb more of the heat rays than others. Black, for example, increases the absorption of heat. If, therefore, they could have dyed the water black, they could have borrowed more heat from the sun. That was not found practicable, but Dr. Bloch, a distinguished chemist, introduced a green dye which was almost, but not quite, as good as black as a heat conductor. The salt water tanks were covered with a layer of fresh water, dyed green. Because of the density of the Dead Sea water, the two layers do not mix, but the dyed surface water admits the heat rays and rapidly heats up the salt water underneath. They went further than this. As a sideline they took advantage of the same idea and of the difference between the temperatures of the top and bottom waters to develop a heat engine for mechanical purposes.

To use nylon in the way they propose would be a costly business if the Israelis had to buy their nylon, as you and I do, in the shops. They do not propose to. They intend to get their nylon from the desert itself.

One of the commonest and hardiest plants in the desert is the castor oil plant, and those who only know, and probably dislike it as medicine, will not see much connection between castor oil and nylon. But the scientists at the Weizmann Institute know about fermentation, on which the President himself is one of the world's greatest experts. Fermentation means using natural organisms, like germs or fungi, to break up vegetable matter into its chemical parts. By fermentation the castor oil plant can become the source of plastics—including nylon, which at the moment comes from either coal or petroleum. But after all, coal and petroleum are just vegetation (like the castor oil plant) which has been hoarded, crushed and transformed in the course of millions of years. Using the fermentation to speed up these long-drawn-out processes, the scientists mean to get an annual harvest of plastics, from the desert. They mean to put the desert to work in terms of modern industry, and Dr. Ernest David Bergman, the Director of the Weizmann Institute, believes that the castor oil plant will become at least as important as the oranges and lemons industry in the future economy of Israel. That is an important consideration in a country which has no mineral resources and which is half desert.

Their own experience in the 80 years since the beginning of the return of the Jews to Palestine and their present researches have encouraged the Israelis in the belief that they can get useful crops out of the desert.

One remarkable example which I was shown at the Weizmann Institute impressed me. It was just three trays of sand. In this book and on my travels I have talked a lot about the 'fertility' of the desert, but there were times when I looked at a vast expanse of sand and thought 'This, at least, is hopeless.' But in those three trays I had the answer. They were all from the same plot—a sand dune. The first tray contained sand as fine as is used in an egg-timer; the second, a year later, contained lumps—it was becoming soil; in the third tray, at the end of the second year, the lumps were bigger and contained some *humus,* decomposing vegetable matter; the sand was becoming fertile.

Now the only treatment this sand had had over two years was irrigation, with water which included ordinary artificial fertiliser. The fertilisers were in the same proportions as were used elsewhere in the area on productive soil. The sand did not receive any more water, or fertiliser, than the other productive plots around. The only difference was that the same amount of water and fertiliser was spread more often throughout the day than is usual in normal irrigation. Yet the sand began to knit into the soil, good soil on which crops are now growing.

This shows what can be done by soil chemistry and soil biology. The chemists knew what the sand lacked in mineral content and the biologists knew how to coax back life into the sand—because soil is a living thing and not just a collection of minerals.

On my journeys I was accompanied by Israeli Government experts, like Dr. Goldslager, the Director of Soil Conservation, whom I have already mentioned. Goldslager was typical of these experts. He is a high-ranking official on whose work a great deal of the future prosperity of Israel depends. Yet to meet him you would have thought he was one of his own landworkers. He wore battledress—khaki blouse and trousers—and was quite capable of leaping on to the seat of a tractor to show a settler how contour ploughing ought to be done. He had made extensive journeys abroad to study soil conservation methods and was a student of Professor Lowdermilk whom we shall meet later.

But Goldslager still remains a humble member of his *kibbutz* or collective settlement. To understand what is happening in Israel, it is necessary to know something about the *kibbutzim* (the plural of *kibbutz*). A *kibbutz* is a pattern of farming and of living. There are different ways of living in rural Israel, apart from the *kibbutzim.* For example, there is the *moshav,* where the people get a piece of land from the

Jewish National Fund. Each piece of land is just enough for one family, including children, to farm. Each family produces enough for its own subsistence and if there is a surplus it is sold co-operatively and the proceeds are shared. It is forbidden to employ labour—no one can hire another man's services —but there is a 'good deed' system by which the individual farmers in the *moshav* help each other in times of stress or in times of need. There are communal buildings, such as the meeting-place, the clinic, the school, the hospital, and they may combine to buy and run farm implements which would be beyond the means of an individual farmer—such as a tractor or a harvester. They live their own lives in their own homes and they farm their section as though it were their own. The land is, for all practical purposes, theirs for 49 years. Then, according to the Biblical practice of the *jubilee*, the land reverts to the community, but, if it has been properly worked, it will be leased to them again.

Then there is the *shitufia*, which is a 'non-communal collective'. That is to say, they work the land in common, as a group, but they live a family life at home, eating and sleeping and bringing up their family in their own house. But even there the housewife has to give a certain number of hours a month to working with the group.

There is still another variant, where the land is privately owned either by the farmers or by landlords, who work the land through tenants, just like the practice in the British countryside, although to create the community life so needed by Israel, they live together in townships, rather than in farmhouses.

The *kibbutz*, however, is the basic pattern of development of the land in Israel. A *kibbutz* is a completely communal affair. The land is collectively owned and worked. The equipment belongs to the community. Even the clothes the members wear are supplied by the *kibbutz* and the garments are drawn from what, in the army, would be the Quartermaster's Store. This may lead to the men dressing very much alike, but somehow the women manage to choose clothes which suit them and are different, although the fashions in blouses and shorts and kerchiefs may by Parisian standards be rather limited. They eat together in the communal dining-room. They sleep in domitories, or, in the case of married couples, in cubicles.

The children do not live with their parents. They are the trust, and a very special one, of the community. In every *kibbutz* the emphasis is on the care and schooling of the children. Since the father and mother both have to work, the children are removed to a crèche for infants, to a nursery school for the toddlers and to a teaching school for the older children. The children have a life apart from their parents, except between the end of the working day and the children's bedtime and at the holidays, when the family gets together.

Joining, or creating, a *kibbutz* is an act of dedication. The setting up of a *kibbutz* is preceded by a probationary period for those who propose to form it and to live and work together. They may form a trial community in one of the big reception camps in which immigrants are housed on their arrival; or they may hive off from an existing *kibbutz*, like bees swarming. The important thing is that no matter what their background, or where they came from, or even their languages (of which there are 37 amongst the Jewish immigrants, coming, as they do, from every corner of the world, including China, the middle of the Sahara, and Yemen), they must be able to get along together. Quarrels and tantrums would wreck a *kibbutz*. When they have proved that they can get along together, the Jewish Agency or the Jewish National Fund will provide them with the land, the bare necessities, and the expert advice for starting a settlement. From there on, it is entirely a matter for the group. The little luxuries, the improved amenities, the further equipment and the cultural advancement of the *kibbutz* members and their families depend entirely on their own efforts.

Some *kibbutzim* are large and wealthy; they will even send their children abroad for higher education, for training in art or music, and to bring out their talents. One of the old-established *kibbutzim*, Ein Herod, the biggest in the country, has 1,500 members. It has a museum of Jewish art, collected from all over the world. It has a large hall and a convalescent home which they make available to members of the Jewish Trade Union movement.

On the other hand, I went to visit a new *kibbutz* at Mansoura, on the borders of Syria, in the extreme north. We had some difficulty getting there, because we found ourselves in the Huleh Marshes at dusk and we were supposed to be sleeping at Mansoura, but no one could tell us whether there was even a decent road to it. There was quite a good one, but only for part of the way. So in pitch darkness we found ourselves stranded in the mountains at a dead end and had to abandon the car and try to grope our way over the hills to Mansoura (now renamed *Kfar Hanassi*, 'The Village of the President').

It was an unpleasant experience, because we had lost our bearings, and while we could see lights in the mountains, we could not be sure whether they represented Jewish or Syrian outposts. In either case, stragglers at night would have short shrift from border guards in an area where armed marauders operate. In fact, it was touch-and-go because we ran straight into the sten gun of a sentry who was (not unnaturally) as nervous as we were, only he had his finger on the trigger. Fortunately, he was an Australian immigrant and we managed to get in a shouted explanation before he fired. He agreed to escort us to Mansoura, which meant a laborious climb over and down the mountains, tripping over boulders and being warned all the time that there were mines and booby traps around from past battles. Even in the dark I realised what a desolate place this boulder-strewn *kibbutz* must be.

But we had a boisterous welcome from the young people, lads and girls, ex-commandoes who were starting this experiment in living, or, for the time being, experiment in existing. They were all English-speaking immigrants, British, Australian, South African and Canadian, and most of them sounded as though they came from Glasgow. They were all Social Democrats: these *kibbutizm* can take their groupings from political sympathies or from religious persuasions. That night I shared a tent with a bearded marine engineer from the Clyde shipyards.

Next morning we drove over the trackless mountains, to where we had abandoned our car, in the truck which was taking the milk to the co-operative centre. Then I knew that my impression formed in the darkness was an under-estimate of the actual conditions with which these youngsters had to struggle. The whole *kibbutz* was a mass of boulders. They had bulldozers and tractors, but in the end it depended on their bare hands—to collect and pile the rocks. Apart from this laborious chore of clearing the ground before they could even start ploughing, they had to earn the money with which to equip themselves and their *kibbutz*. This they have done, on the one hand, by starting a foundry—because they happened to have a B.Sc. metallurgist from Birmingham and some engineers, like my tent-mate. They started at first to make their own parts for the pipeline, which brings their water supply from the hills, but then they began to get orders from surrounding *kibbutzim*, which were willing to pay for brass and iron fittings. Another source of income was hiring themselves as labour to the *kibbutz* at Afikim, at the south end of the Sea of Galilee. There a settlement, agricultural in origin, has developed a large factory for the making of plywood for the whole of Israel.

No one in a *kibbutz* gets any wages, but an industrial *kibbutz* like Afikim can borrow workers from surrounding settlements and pay their wages into the funds of their parent settlement. So by trading surpluses, leasing labour and developing a useful industry, a *kibbutz* can acquire the money for its agricultural needs. The first principle is developing the land feeding first their own people, then the people of Israel, and then, like the citrus-growing *kibbutzim*, going into the world-markets.

When a person joins a *kibbutz*, or is born into one, he belongs to it as completely as any member of a monastic order. He can leave, but it is a momentous choice, or he can be expelled, which is extremely rare. The children are admitted as formal members of the *kibbutz* at the age of 17. They can then

L

vote with their elders on all the affairs of the settlement, or they can decide to leave if they choose. The student from a *kibbutz* sent abroad returns, at least in principle, as an ordinary member of the settlement, called upon to do the heavy labours of the settlement and to give of his talents to the culture of his *kibbutz*, but at the end of a year he may, with the blessing of the others, decide to leave and follow a career.

To return to Dr. Goldslager: By formal vote of his *kibbutz*, he, with his special abilities, has been loaned to the Government, like most of the experts in Government service—even in foreign affairs. By a reverse vote, he or they can be recalled to the service of the settlements. Whenever his government duties allow him, he returns to work in his *kibbutz*, where his family still is. The week-end of an Israeli civil servant is no off-time. Many of them have their *kibbutz* duties to attend to.

The uniformity of *kibbutz* life does not extend to its business relations. If a settlement has negotiations or trading deals, or a trading agency to establish for its products, the member who is chosen by the vote of his colleagues will be given tailor-made clothes, a substantial expense account and perhaps even a luxury car, out of the settlement funds. As long as he is in a world outside the *kibbutz*, he can have all the appearance of a successful business man, but he may have to return to the plough at the behest of his settlement. What impresses one about these experts of, and from, the settlements is that they have 'come out of the soil'. They are practical men who served a hard apprenticeship before they acquired academic and technological training. They know the practical problems which beset every farmer, and yet with the zest of pioneers they are not hog-tied by habit and are open to bold and ambitious experiments—like the Lowdermilk Plan for the Jordan Valley which involves, among other things, driving a canal which will admit the Mediterranean to the Jordan Valley.

Professor Walter C. Lowdermilk is not a Jew, although his name is closely identified with Palestine, because he has concerned himself so much with its practical problems. He is an American soil conservationist who has studied erosion and man-made deserts in 38 countries. In 1939, when he was assistant director of the U.S. Government Soil Conservation Service, he set out to learn in the areas of the old civilisations lessons which would be valuable to his own country—the U.S.A. There our American contemporaries succeeded in doing in 30 years what was spread over 3,000 years in the Old World—produced deserts by the wholesale destruction of forests and soil. The dust which curtained New York at midday—soil blown from the Dust Bowl of Oklahoma and the Dakotas—was an omen to our day and generation.

Fortunately, the Americans heeded the omen and men like Lowdermilk were given the chance to develop soil-saving schemes, which not only checked the destruction but in large measure helped to salvage the Lost Lands. He made a tour of North Africa and the Middle East, which was almost identical with my own. He had already had the experience of China and elsewhere and he finished up in Palestine.

Professor Lowdermilk is a devout Christian and a Bible student. Palestine to him was not just another slice of desert, but the Holy Land—a land flowing with milk and honey— which had fallen into decay. His was not just a survey, it was a pilgrimage, and for him something of an emotional crisis, because he saw the victims of Nazi persecution being denied refuge in what they regarded as their National Home. He saw also 300 settlements of Jews, defying hardships, practising co-operation and restoring the land which had been lying waste for centuries. They had transformed reeking malarial swamps into prosperous farms and orange groves and had built a great city—Tel Aviv—on what thirty years before had been a waste of creeping sand-dunes.

Professor Lowdermilk produced a scheme for the recovery of Palestine. He recognised its two primary needs—water and power. The main source of both could be the Jordan. The sweet waters of the river and of its tributaries, the Yarmuk and the Zerqa, flowing in from the east, descend through the great rift to the Dead Sea 1,292 ft. below sea level.

He suggested diverting the sweet waters of the Jordan and its tributaries away from the salt-trough of the Dead Sea and into a system of canals running round the slopes of the Jordan

Valley and irrigating about 155,000 acres of good land. The Jordan, however, has more water than would be required for that. It could irrigate five times as much land as the valley itself offers. This surplus, he suggested, should be removed in the area of Lake Huleh, north of the Galilee. Huleh is now a malarial swamp and a series of peat bogs. A large proportion of the available water is squandered in this soggy wasteland, and it could be drained off and diverted into the fertile plains of Esdraelon and Beisan on the west side of the Jordan. Huleh could then become a reclamation area. Much of the land, now water-bound, could be easily made productive and even the peat bogs do not scare the Israeli scientists. For one thing, they use dry peat from the Huleh to help change the properties of the soil elsewhere and convert loose sand into soil.

Having taken away the fresh water, Lowdermilk proposed to fill up the Dead Sea by an ambitious scheme for channeling and piping water from the Mediterranean, at Haifa, into the Jordan depression, using the 1,200 ft. drop into the canyon as a waterfall for making electricity. He reckoned that power amounting to about 1,000 million kilowatt-hours a year could be produced.

The Jordan Valley is about 25 miles from Haifa. He proposed that the water should be led by open canal for some seven miles from Haifa to Mount Carmel and then through a tunnel 20 miles long under the Plain of Esdraelon to the valley.

All this was before the existence of the State of Israel and assumed co-operation internationally between Syria, Lebanon, Trans-Jordan, now the Hashimite kingdom of Jordan, and Jewish Palestine. Since then there has been the Jewish-Arab war and the establishment of a Hashimite Kingdom bulging into Palestine, well beyond the Jordan. Only about one-third of the valley and a third of the Dead Sea are in Jewish hands. The original scheme included the restoration of what was once useful land on the Trans-Jordan side. Under the new conditions the Lowdermilk scheme needs either revision or a new compromise between Jew and Arab.

Professor Lowdermilk was the chairman of the Commission

on the Arid Zone which Unesco called in Paris and from which my mission sprang. He was then concentrating on the deserts of Africa south of the Equator. Fortunately our paths met in Palestine and we were able to compare notes on desert problems, and I was also able to discuss with him on the ground the new problems of the 'J.V.A.'—the Jordan equivalent of the Tennessee Valley Authority. We had agreed to meet at the Sea of Galilee.

When the descent to the Sea of Galilee began, I felt a clamour of mixed sensations. For one thing, my ears started 'popping' the way they do in an aeroplane when it is descending; and for the same reason, changing pressure—Galilee is 682 ft. below sea level. For another, the road was steep and twisting enough to make me feel nervous. And those physical sensations were all confused with emotional ones. The clouds had been piling up over the Jordan Valley and the landscape was a conflict of sun and shadow, with the Sea of Galilee shimmering and seagulls signalling with their white wings, while the storm brooded over Bashan, the plateau across the Jordan. Over there was an isolated Jewish outpost, the settlement of Ein Gev, which is a *kibbutz* for intellectuals who till the soil —and man the defences, because a few hundred feet above, looking down on the settlement, are the Syrian lines manned by the Arab Legion. Here was a rift, political as well as geological.

There was another conflict within me. I looked at the broad expanse of this freshwater sea, with the fishing boats heeling and tossing in the gathering storm, and wondered what it would look like if, in ten years' time, it had shrunk to half its size. At least one of the schemes alternative to the original Lowdermilk plan would involve that—depriving the Sea of Galilee of half its water.

After I had been over the ground with Professor Lowdermilk, I went to Jerusalem for discussions on the Jordan Valley Scheme with the Israeli planners. My visit to Jerusalem at that period was an experience quite different from what one would normally associate with the Holy City—the Holy City of Jew, Christian and Mohammedan.

The boundary of Jordan and Israel runs through the town of Jerusalem. No Man's Land in some places is just the breadth of a street, but having lost my right of access to Jordan by having an Israeli stamp on my passport, the gulf was as wide as the Atlantic.

I knew the Israelis were in possession of the New City and that the Old City, with all the Holy Places, was in the hands of the Arabs. But I was agreeably surprised by the New City. I think it was the effect of well-proportioned new buildings, built of hewn stone—a stone with a warm pink colour. There are no brick or concrete buildings in Jerusalem. There is a law against it. It was a British edict, to keep the character of the city. But the Israelis have maintained it.

In December 1949, Dr. de Leeuw, who had come originally from Holland, brought together a team of engineers from all over the world to produce a programme for the irrigation of Palestine, including the Jordan Valley scheme. With the changes in the geography of Palestine, because of the awkward frontiers of Trans-Jordan and the difficulties of coming to terms with the Arabs, Lowdermilk's original scheme needed a lot of changes, although Lowdermilk still maintained that nothing ought to be done which would prevent some later co-operation with the surrounding States.

He had in mind the example of the Tennessee Valley Authority where seven States were involved. It was true that they were all members of the United States, but the Federal Government had few rights of intervention in the domestic affairs of these States. It was only because flood control happened to be the concern of the U.S. Army Engineers that the Federal Government had any excuse for stepping into it. Flood control, however, means big dams and big dams mean not only controlled water for irrigation purposes, but also hydro-electricity, and the abundance of electricity completely changed the character of the States of the Tennessee Valley. Maybe J.V.A. would, in the same way, do a lot to overcome passions and politics in the Middle East.

Whether or not a compromise could be reached with the Arab States, those Israelis with whom I talked were quite determined to go through with a programme. The first steps were the purely local ones of providing wells for particular districts and for using water within the inner limits of the State—like the scheme which included harnessing the River Yarkon, which runs into the sea near Tel Aviv, and also the coastal wells in that area. This scheme could be self-contained. Nevertheless, it was entirely designed to fit into a Jordan Valley scheme ultimately.

Even this Yarkon scheme is an impressive one. It involves carrying water by pipeline from the Tel Aviv area to the Negev and supplying Jerusalem on the way. The water supply of Jerusalem is precarious. All houses have rain-catching cisterns, but the main supply used to come from the wells at Bethlehem about five miles away. Bethlehem is now in Arab territory and the New City is cut off from that source. So the Israelis have to carry the water over 60 miles instead of five.

From the Yarkon area, two huge pipelines will carry the water to the desert. One pipeline runs through the coastal belt and the other, the eastern line, has a branch supply to Jerusalem on its way to the desert. The western pipe, for irrigation, is intended to carry the sewage of Tel Aviv, plus the water from the Yarkon, into the Negev over 75 miles away. It was a surprising sight to see in the desert a great, lonely mechanical digger gnawing out, a ton at a bite, the trenches for the pipeline.

All schemes for irrigation and well sinking have to fit into the Master Plan. This Master Plan, the eventual J.V.A., provides five different versions of the original Lowdermilk scheme. Under one scheme the Mediterranean would be carried from Haifa to the Dead Sea without touching Jordan, which would involve a very long canal unless Arab agreement can be obtained. A second would run from Haifa to a point in the Jordan just within the frontiers of Israel. A third would run from Haifa to a point north of the Sea of Galilee, again within the frontiers of Israel. A fourth would run from the Mediterranean, near Gaza, which is in Egyptian hands, to the Dead Sea. A fifth would start from the other end of

Israel—at Elatt, on the Gulf of Akaba—to the southern end of the Dead Sea. In each case the drop into the rift of the Jordan or the Dead Sea would provide the waterfall for electricity.

There are also various schemes for the use of the sweet water of the Jordan and a £5,000,000 scheme for draining the swamplands of the Huleh, all of which the Israelis can carry out within their own frontiers and without the co-operation of the Arabs.

One such scheme would divert the headwaters of the Jordan from the Huleh area into a depression, Sahl El Battauf, to the west of the Sea of Galilee, which would form a great reservoir. From this the water would be pumped back into the Valley of the Jordan, as well as contribute the supplies for the water grid which finishes up in the Negev.

By diverting the Huleh supplies and by sealing the Jordan outlet from the Sea of Galilee and creating a sweet water canal into the Beisan, the sea would become a small lake, and 20,000 acres of land, now covered with water, would be recovered.

The lake reduced in this way would still remain sweet—or at least it would take 300 years to have a salt content equal to that of the Mediterranean and 1,000 years to become as salt as the Dead Sea.

This drastic reduction of the Sea of Galilee, with its religious associations, will probably not be necessary, but sense and self-interest ought to persuade all the countries around that a combined effort can convert the Jordan into a source of water and power for the benefit of them all.

My visit to Israel was perhaps the most strenuous part of the whole journey. Everyone was so insistent that I should see what was being done and what could be done that I found myself starting at dawn and finishing at two in the morning. On one single day I left a tent on the northernmost frontier at five in the morning and at five in the afternoon I was at Elatt in the Gulf of Akaba. This was a case of 'From Dan to Beersheba—and all stations south'.

The Israelis are convinced that by proper development of a country of which half is desert they could have a population at least twice and probably three times as great as the million who are there today. They believe they can feed and support not only all the refugees who have come in from the countries of Jewish persecution, and the immigrants whom they are collecting from out-of-the-way places, like the Sahara and the Arabian Desert, but many more. This is a claim about which some authorities are sceptical, but Israel is a State founded on an ancient faith and modern science, and these two things do not fit into the figurings and sums of conventional economists.

Palestine has been described as 'the boiling pot of the Middle East'. It is not a boiling pot; it is a pressure cooker. There they are trying to do in one generation what other nations have taken centuries to achieve. They are, for instance, trying to take the people out of the conditions of the 12th century which prevail in Yemen and mix them up with people, like the refugee intellectuals, who represent the latest technical advances of civilisation. Those Yemenites, who are supposed to be the descendants of a colony established by Solomon but who are, according to some experts, the truest surviving specimens of the early Egyptians, had never even seen an aircraft until the Tudor airliner arrived to ferry them to Zion. Now 50,000 of them have been transplanted. In modern Israel there is an endless variety of cultures and languages, which somehow have to be merged into a new community.

Everything is so new that there is no one there who says 'We tried it and it did not work'. Indeed, in the case of the desert and the lessons of the old civilisations which are there in the sands, they are saying 'It worked once, let's try it again'.

# CHAPTER ELEVEN

# POSTSCRIPT TO ADVENTURE

IF you had gone into the Operations Room of a military head-quarters during the Second World War, you might have seen senior officers, with lots of red tabs and 'brass', playing at sand castles, pushing toy tanks around and mounting toy guns. You might have thought that this was all very childish at a serious moment in war. Indeed, it was all very serious, because they would be planning, in miniature, battles in which many men's lives would be involved.

This method of the 'sand-table' could be extremely effective, because in sand, or perhaps in clay, the geography of the battle-field could be reproduced in detail, and difficulties not always obvious in paper-planning could be forestalled.

When I was in Tripolitania, a former senior officer of Montgomery's staff, now an administrator dealing with the kind of problems I was studying, suggested that the sand-table method might be used to make people understand the peculiar behaviour of the desert. He had in mind the desert nomads and their children, whom he had always found extremely ready to learn if they could understand the thing in terms of their own experience. His idea was to have sand-tables imitating a familiar section of the desert, and then to have fans to reproduce the wind and sprays to represent the rain, and heat-lamps to be the sun. In this way it could be shown how dust storms build up, how water erosion starts and how the sun dries and bleaches the soil when there is not any shade.

Having shown these processes, the sand-table could then be used to explain how they could be checked. Model trees would be planted to show their value both as 'umbrellas' to check the rain and as windbreaks to check the winds. Match sticks might be used to illustrate the method of dune-fixing, by planting grasses in squares.

There and then he squatted down in the desert and, spreading out his roadmap, he improvised on it a sand-table roughly like the part of the desert we were in. He then drew lines like plough furrows. The sand was whipped off. He did it again across the line of the 'prevailing wind' and showed how the cross-furrows checked the drift. Then, using the exhaust of the jeep, he improvised a desert storm and showed how the dunes began to form and to move. It was all childishly simple but it had many lessons to teach.

By the time I travelled thousands and thousands of miles across deserts, I began to feel the need of a sand-table—some way of seeing all the various problems in a model form: Cyprus became my sand-table.

Cyprus, for this purpose, is remarkably useful. It is an island in the Eastern Mediterranean lying 240 miles north of Egypt, 60 miles west of Lebanon, and 40 miles south of Turkey, the coastline of which is clearly visible from it. Its area is 3,500 square miles, less than half that of Wales.

There were people living in Cyprus as long ago as 4,000 B.C. and at various times it has been ruled by the Assyrians, the Persians, the Egyptians, the Romans, the Byzantines, the Venetians, the Turks, and now the British. It bears the imprint of all these civilisations, as well as being rich in even earlier remains. There is all the evidence in its suffering soil of the havoc that was wrought all through the centuries.

Christianity was introduced to the island by St. Paul in A.D. 45 and it was a base for the Crusades. In 1191 Richard the Lion Heart of England, while on his way to the Holy Land, seized the island. Later he transferred it to the Order of Knights of Templar for £100,000, but unfortunately the Templars could not pay their debt, so Richard gave the island to Guy de Lusignan, the ex-King of Jerusalem, whose family ruled the island for nearly 300 years. Then the Genoese and later the Venetians controlled the island. Shakespeare's tragedy *Othello* was based on the Venetian occupation of Cyprus. A tower near the present Customs House of Famagusta is still pointed out as the place where Othello smothered Desdemona. In 1570 the Turks captured the island and ruled it for 300 years. In 1878, although it was still nominally

Turkish, Cyprus came under British administration, and in 1925 was made a Crown Colony.

Cyprus is not strictly an 'arid zone'. The mean annual rainfall which varies from season to season and from one locality to another even in this small area, ranges from 8 inches in the lowlands to 45 inches in the mountains.

It usually falls in heavy and localised storms, which never last long. From April to October, there is usually no rain at all. The extremes of climate and the occasional but fierce downpours expose the island to serious soil destruction. That is obvious from the air when one is flying into Cyprus, because for miles around the island the Mediterranean blue of the sea is clouded with mud, swept down by the river torrents, which for most of the year are dry beds.

The climate is one factor, but men, by centuries of mismanagement, have been a more serious one. At one time the island had a population of at least a million, but invasions, droughts, famine, plagues, swarms of locusts and frequent massacres reduced it to about 80,000 in 1792. The present population is roughly half-a-million, but it is estimated that by A.D. 2,000 it will be again a million.

So here, almost at a glance, or at least in a few days' touring of the island, one can get a distinct picture of how man-made deserts are produced and also how they can be recovered.

The story of recovery from all the centuries of misuse of the soil is a remarkable one which belongs mainly to the last thirty years and particularly to the last ten years.

From the moment the plane touches down on Nicosia Airport, a visitor realises, or ought to, that there is a battle being waged in which he himself has to play a passive but important part. The aircraft is immediately boarded by 'gunmen', but the guns they carry are deadly only to mosquitoes. They spray the passengers and the aircraft in case some mosquito has stowed away aboard. No mosquito must be allowed to land in Cyprus.

The cabin of the aircraft is kept locked for some time with the passengers in it. My neighbour, who had come through from Baghdad, was furious at the delay and the indignity of what he called being 'de-loused'. I gave him a penny lecture about Mesopotamia from which he had come, about the death of Alexander the Great from malaria on the banks of the Euphrates at Babylon, and how the deserts with which he was familiar, because he was an irrigation engineer, had been produced with the help of the mosquitoes, because a disease-crippled population could not maintain irrigation or cultivation.

In Cyprus malaria has been wiped out by one of the most spectacular health campaigns in history. In three years the mosquito and its malarial parasite, which had ravaged the island for centuries, was banished. On January 10th, 1950, it was possible to announce with a flourish of trumpets 'Malaria has been defeated'.

Before the war, more than 18,000 cases of malaria a year were recorded at Cyprus. Out of every 1,000 babies, 180 used to die of malaria every year. Today there are no new cases . . .

There was a friendly competition between Cyprus and the Italian island of Sardinia, which, starting at the same time, was waging a similar battle against mosquitoes. At the end of 1948, the High Commissioner of Sardinia offered the Governor of Cyprus a wager that his island would be free of malaria first. The wager was 100 bottles of wine. Cyprus won.

This remarkable achievement was due to the health services under Dr. Horace Shelley, but the Great Liberator, as he has been called, was Mr. Mehmed Aziz, a Cypriot who had worked under Sir Ronald Ross, the man who first discovered the part which the mosquito played in the disease. He organised a staff of 770. He divided the island into six districts, sub-divided into 39 sections, 111 zones and 56 blocks. Every single mosquito breeding place in every one of these blocks was sprayed with mosquito-killing chemical D.D.T. once every 12 days until there was no trace of the enemy. An island was freed from deadly menace at a cost of £300,000—just 13/- per head of the population.

Another invader which Cyprus has to fight is the locust, the flying insect, the giant grasshopper which takes wings. Unfortunately the fighters in Cyprus cannot, as in the case of the mosquito, get at the breeding places of the locusts which may be thousands of miles away, on the Red Sea or even in Morocco. They can only cope with them when they arrive by an effective locust-fighting service.

Cyprus, however, has its own locusts—the goats which they call 'The Black Locusts', because they devour and destroy every bit of green foliage they can get hold of. This is a more tricky problem than either the mosquito or the locust, because the islanders for centuries have cherished their goats. The shepherd is an old and difficult institution in island life. He may have his own herd but he will also look after the sheep and goats of others. He has been accustomed to drive his flocks wherever he liked, regardless of the damage he might do. In much the same category are the charcoal burners and the lime-burners. The island has no coal or fuel other than wood. Wood from the forests has been used indiscriminately, and in the case of the giant limekilns which look like miniature volcanoes, extravagantly used.

Today it is law that no wood must be used for producing lime. Oil burners must be substituted and the use of oil for domestic purposes is also being encouraged and extended.

How to tackle the problem of the free-roaming shepherd almost defeated the authorities until, on August 23rd, 1938, the abbot and monks of the powerful Kykko Monastery agreed to renounce all their grazing privileges and remove their goat flocks from the State forests in return for cash payment. This was a red-letter day because the deadlock was broken and other graziers followed the example of the monks. It meant the first big advance towards the restoration of the forests of Cyprus, which had been systematically and repeatedly destroyed, because the lawless shepherds, merely in order to get low-bush growth which they regarded as better goat fodder, would deliberately set fire to the forests. They did not consider it a crime—although sometimes it was an act of vengeance against the authorities who were trying to limit their grazing.

From a forest look-out—a fire watcher's post 2,000 feet up on top of a mountain—I looked down and saw the remarkable results which merely the restriction of goat grazing could pro-

duce. Below me the mountains were beginning to sprout trees
—pines, oaks, cedars and the cypresses of Cyprus which were
becoming gradually extinct. Forests were thrusting up out of
the ground without a single tree having been planted. This
was Nature's resistance movement which had gone underground under the persecution of the goat and, the moment
the enemy was removed, emerged into the open.

Trees have been planted—thousands of them. They have
been planted round villages, as what are known as 'village
fuel areas', where the villagers have agreed to keep off the
goats and not to cut down the trees until they have had a
chance to grow. In a few years the villagers will, by proper
management and cutting, have their fuel and the woods as
well.

Trees have also been planted on the barren hillsides which
were stripped bare and which drained the rains into those
torrential gullies through which the soil sweeps to the sea.
The trees have been planted to check this erosion.

By controlling the waters by dams and irrigation systems,
by persuading the farmers to till their land in ways which will
prevent it from being washed or blown away, and by a variety
of methods which, in one form or another, I had seen all over
North Africa and the Middle East, the soil conservation experts of Cyprus have, in the last few years, nursed hundreds
of thousands of sick acres back to health. The work goes on
all the time and the lowland deserts of Cyprus are emerging
again as rich productive lands.

Standing on that mountain top in the middle of Cyprus,
after all my wanderings in the wilderness, I felt that I was
looking at the prospect of a Promised Land—a desert which
could be made to flow with milk and honey.

But the land is only *promised*. Men must make good that
promise. In Cyprus, within the confines of a small island, one
could see what was possible when men have the right kind of
ideas, are willing to learn from the mistakes (and the
experience) of the past, are prepared to use properly modern
mechanised methods, and to work hard.

While I was in Cyprus, I borrowed a dictionary, just an

ordinary English dictionary, to look up the word 'desert'. It was a bit late in the day, considering all the thousands of miles of desert I had crossed without the benefit of any dictionary-definition, but it was useful because it reminded me that in this strange language of ours 'desert' had three quite different meanings. As a verb, it means 'To abandon in time of need or in violation of duty'. As a noun, it can mean either 'An arid region lacking in moisture to support vegetation' or 'The reward or punishment one deserves'.

So, if we desert the deserts, we shall get our deserts!

This is certainly a 'time of need', because although there is a great deal of food in some parts of the world and Europe, for example, has restored its farming which was so hurt by the war, there are about a thousand million people in the world who do not get enough to eat. Now the number of people in the world is increasing at the rate of one more mouth to feed every one-and-a-half seconds all day and all night, week in, week out, and Lord Boyd Orr, who won the Nobel Peace Prize because he fought the battle for food, has warned us that it is our duty to produce, by 1965, at least twice as much food as we do today. Only by that means will there be a chance for everyone to get enough to eat. We have also to bear in mind that the people who are short of food are those in what are called the 'underdeveloped areas' where there is a lot of trouble brewing because they are beginning to realise that their children need not die of hunger since it is actually possible to produce food for them—or to stop the food they produce from going to better-off countries. That is quite right, but it means that countries like Britain, which have to get the bigger part of their food from overseas because they do not grow enough themselves, are going to find it awkward. If a *gaucho* of the Argentine decides to eat his own steaks, then a British family goes short on its ration.

So the deserts are much nearer to Britain than we would imagine from looking at the maps, for in years to come our food supplies will depend on the total world supplies. If there is a shortage anywhere we are likely to feel the squeeze. If, on the other hand, countries are able not only to meet their own needs and the needs of their next-door neighbours (I have in mind the possibilities of Persia helping to feed the teeming millions of the Indian sub-continent) but to export, then we will be able to get our share. It is, therefore, very much a bread-and-butter concern of Britain to encourage the fertility of the deserts. It is, also, very much in the interest of all the other nations as well, because if people cannot get food there is bound to be trouble, and the kind of trouble which will lead to wars.

It is not going to be easy to deal with this desert problem, because people in many of these desert parts are suspicious of the motives which make wealthy nations offer their help; they are not sure that it is for their own good. For instance, what I saw of the desert-reclamation schemes in French North Africa was exciting and sensible, but the desert tribes need a lot of persuading. When I described that scheme for draining the Southern Marsh in Algeria, and taking the water through the Atlas to the coastal plains, some Arabs said 'Yes, taking away the water from the tribes and giving it to the Europeanised settlers on the coast'.

It is quite true that the fertile lands of the coast will benefit, but the scheme also means more waterholes for the wandering herds of the High Plains. Indeed, it is the concern of the French to see that the desert tribes get enough water and enough land to settle on, because if they begin to drift, as they are doing, out of the Sahara and into the settled areas, they can cause difficulties, especially if they merely become unemployed at the ports. When I explained that, the same Arabs said 'Yes, they want to condemn the tribes to live only in the desert'.

From my own observations, I should have thought it would have been difficult to persuade the tribes to leave the deserts, but it is all a matter of point of view.

This human problem of men and their habits in the desert is one of the biggest difficulties in tackling its recovery. I can say quite definitely that vast areas of the desert which I saw had been made by men and their animals, helped, of course, by extremes of climate which quickly spreads any havoc men

M

create. It is not always possible, as it has been in Cyprus, to persuade people to give up age-old habits (like keeping free-roving goats) and accept 'newfangled' ideas. It takes time to convince tribal chiefs that a fleet of tractors might make an even more impressive show of wealth and circumstance than a herd of camels. It will take much persuasion to convince nomads with a tradition of wandering which goes back thousands of years that settled farming is to be preferred to roving.

Every expert on desert-reclamation whom I met put 'men and their habits' first on the list of problems—before finding water, even. That is reasonable, because 'men and their habits' have helped to make finding water difficult. That business of destroying trees and covering-growth makes the water spill off in wasteful spates instead of soaking into the ground to feed the underground springs, so that its effects may be found in a dying oasis hundreds of miles away.

When we think of the desert in terms of rainfall, we should bear in mind that insistence of the French scientists—'We are walking on water'. Water should not be restricted to the idea of something which drops from the sky, although that is useful. There are underground seams, those spongy layers which drain the rain which falls in the mountains into water supplies deep beneath the surface—like the 'Albienne Nappe', the vast buried lake beneath the Sahara. The problem is how to get down to it and release it so that it can water the surface soil. That is a matter of boring wells, often to depths as great as those of oil wells. Oil, however, is 'liquid gold' and water is just water, too expensive for irrigation if it has to be pumped more than a few feet.

We must also bear in mind that even spate water can be controlled and used. The *wadhis* are considerable, if short-lived, rivers which flow into a sea of sand and get wasted. But, if they are dammed and directed, they can spread over soil which can produce good crops.

Then there are all the lessons to be learned from the Ancients—those Roman wells and cisterns, the diversion dams and terraces.

Even more provoking to the imagination is the matter of

dew. To wade in the hot dry sand of a dune and be told there is water underneath requires some stretch of imagination. But, after all, these dunes advance not *on* rollers but *as* rollers, not by shifting bodily but through the sand being blown onwards as a spray of dust, or acting like slow-moving waves tumbling over each other. They have a base which is either a rock formation, a buried palmery, or the water-logged sand itself. If, by means of *foggaras,* those horizontal wells, or something like them, we could drain water out of the spongy dunes, there could be a water-supply even in the sand-desert. Or we might employ devices like the pebble-mounds of the Negev which condense moisture out of the atmosphere of a rainless desert. Perhaps modern ingenuity could produce 'prefab' dew-mounds.

With the problem of finding water, we have to consider the question of salting. Often it is a question of sinking a well in the wrong place so that the water comes up through salty rocks, while a few hundred yards away the same fresh-water source could be tapped without any such misadventure. That does not solve the difficulties of a natural spring, like the one at Taghit, which leaves a fraction of salt continuously in the soil as it evaporates, turns the soil salt and then causes the water itself to become salt through flowing through the soil.

One way is the device I saw in Tunisia of carrying the water from the spring in concrete troughs above the salt soil, but I am sure, if the chemists were really set to work on it, they could find some method, similar to the water-softening process used in homes and in industry, by which the salt could be removed from spring-water as it emerges. Most likely the answer to this kind of problem does not lie in a desert-research station but in some chemical laboratory thousands of miles away—perhaps even in rainy Lancashire where all the time chemists are having to find ways of treating water for the use of the cotton-mills.

Bound up with all this is the question of fuel. Nobody should blame the modern nomads for cutting down trees or scrub to cook their food and keep themselves warm. The Sahara, for instance, is a much bigger and, indeed, colder place than Cyprus, and it would be a much more expensive business to issue all the tribes with oil stoves and the regular supplies of oil to burn in them.

So even the most ambitious schemes for planting trees in the deserts must take account of this need and the risks of destruction which goes with it. We are inclined to pooh-pooh the idea of solar energy. That is because we live in a climate where sunshine is occasional and irregular, but in the hot deserts, where the sun is constant, unloading energy throughout all the hours of daylight, we would take the sun much more seriously.

As one of the desert-scientists said, it would be useful if physicists would take a few hours off from atomic bombs and give their minds to ways of harnessing the sun so that it could be put to work to give warmth to people in the hours of darkness and to bore wells and pump water.

Then there are the desert-animals. I must confess it had not occurred to me what an important part animals could play in the recovery of the deserts until I saw the opposite effect— the part which goats play in the creation, or extension, of deserts. I had thought, of course, of the value of camels, but not of breeding other animals to make better use of the deserts. So animal-breeders are 'men against the desert' as much as those who are fixing dunes or discovering water. That is why the experience of the animal-breeding stations at Sidi Mesri, Burg El Arab and Baghdad was so revealing— breeding animals which for the same amount of fodder will give twice as much milk or eggs or beef. Nor must we forget that animals can help to increase the soil-fertility of the desert by providing farm manure.

Last but not least, there are trees, shrubs and vegetation. Once we can stop thinking, as Vic Maitland complained, that there is something absurd about planting trees in the desert, a great deal can be done not only to restore but to extend the forest areas which once existed—'extend' because we can, as the Ancients could not, borrow trees and plants from new worlds which they never knew existed—the Americas and Australia—which can be adapted to an existence in which they have to reach their roots down underground to find the water they cannot get from the sky, or can store, as in the case of the cacti, moisture in their fleshy leaves. And, just as plant-breeders extended wheat-growing into the cold areas of Canada or Siberia where, by previous standards, the rainfall and the extremes of climate would have made it impossible, so they can 'invent' plants which will be suitable and productive in the deserts.

These are only some of the many ways in which the desert problems will have to be tackled. There can be no Master Plan because the various areas present different difficulties and only by really getting to know the peculiarities of a locality can we 'play along' with Nature.

The first thing to realise is that a desert is not just a blank space in a school-atlas, that while a lot of it may be hopeless, much of it is not, and that if we are going to feed hungry people we can, or should, make use of it.

To help to get to know the desert, we ought to realise what came out of it. These areas were not always backward—at least not in the classical deserts which I crossed—but were the cradle of much of our culture and our learning. Much of what we value and prize in our Western Civilisation came out of what we now call 'deserts'.

We should, therefore, try to 'get back to origins' and realise that in recovering these deserts we are, in a way, paying a debt. That is why much of this book has been concerned not just with the scientific job I set out to do or the technical problems I was asked to study, but with what might seem like side-lines, because those of us who have thought about this problem hope to encourage people to follow up their special interests.

These may be geography, history, science, Scripture, litera-ture, mathematics, astronomy, botany, current affairs and so on. My references are no more than clues to be followed up, like the remarks of a guide showing a party round—'And this is where Anne Boleyn had her head chopped off . . . '

I shall always remember that moonlight night above the Kasserine Gap in Tunisia, when Charles Saumagne said: 'Tell me that there are in the world ten men who believe that the desert can be made to blossom—ten men who believe that we can redeem the stupidities of mankind—and I shall die happy'.

I was to travel many thousands more miles across the desert, but at the end of this adventurous journey I could find him, not ten men, but hundreds, and not only men but women, who not only believe but who know and can prove that the desert can be made fruitful.

# INDEX

183

GEORGE ALLEN & UNWIN LTD.
LONDON: 40 MUSEUM STREET, W.C.1
CAPE TOWN: 58–60 LONG STREET
TORONTO: 91 WELLINGTON STREET WEST
BOMBAY: 15 GRAHAM ROAD, BALLARD ESTATE
CALCUTTA: 17 CENTRAL AVENUE, P.O. DHARAMTALA
WELLINGTON, N.Z.: 8 KINGS CRESCENT, LOWER HUTT
SYDNEY, N.S.W.: BRADBURY HOUSE, 55 YORK STREET

# PROFILE OF SCIENCE
## by RITCHIE CALDER

Demy 8vo. 16s. net

Ritchie Calder (science editor of the *News Chronicle*, Council Member of the British Association, United Kingdom delegate to UNESCO) needs no introduction. His name is as familiar to the public as it is in scientific circles where his work has brought him personal acquaintanceship and often friendship with the leading scientists of his generation. Calder's is the outstanding name in British scientific journalism, and in *Profile of Science* he has turned his intimate knowledge of the development of science in his time into a full-length book. In the result we have a study of the major scientific advances of this generation, of the men who primarily initiated them and of how and why these men were enabled to do what they did. It is an immensely readable biographical history of modern science, written from first-hand knowledge by a master expositor, whose accuracy has won the confidence of the scientists of whom he writes.

*Profile of Science* is an experiment in expounding not only the facts of science, but their implications. It deals with the scientists who made the great discoveries as men and not as incredible geniuses. It shows "why they happened" and how they came to make their discoveries. It shows how these discoveries developed and their social and industrial consequences.

The book deals in four main sections with the Atom, Radar, Penicillin, and Vitamins, but related them to the general picture of scientific advance. It begins with Lord Rutherford, the exponent of pure research, and completes the cycle with Sir John Boyd Orr, who carried laboratory facts into world government.

# SCIENCE FOR THE CITIZEN
## by LANCELOT HOGBEN

*New Revised Edition with a Novel Treatment of Atomic Energy*

Demy 8vo. 20s. net

"This is a marvellous book. It is nothing less than an attempt to present the interested layman with the whole fundamental structure of science. No such task has ever been undertaken before; Professor Hogben has not only tried it, but carried it out with a completeness one would not have believed possible. He has brought off one of the most impressive and valuable achievements of our generation."— *The Spectator*.

# SCIENCE : Its Method and Philosophy
## *by* G. BURNISTON BROWN

Demy 8vo.                                                          15*s*. net

Hitherto no book has been written to convey to the educated public
exactly what scientific method is, how it has arisen, and why it is so
much more successful in disclosing new knowledge than any other.
*Science: its method and philosophy* supplies this need.
The form of presentation is evolutionary. Dr. Burniston Brown shows
that the evolution of science is similar to the evolution of animals,
proceeding by jumps and mutations. Consequently no one scientific
method is just a modification of the proceding one, but something
different. Beginning with the learning process in animals, the author
follows with a discussion of words and their meaning. Then he
proceeds to the main theme, the evolution of scientific method from
Aristotle to the present day: the intellectual solidity of the discussion
is, however, lightened and brought close to human life by biographical
details of some of the main figures dealt with.
Dr. Brown's chief aim is to answer clearly three questions: What is
scientific method? How has it arisen? What is a scientific outlook on
the universe in general today? Such a book is much needed today,
where a resurgence of superstition in various forms is creating
problems and confusing issues on which the clearest thinking is
necessary.

# GREEN THRALDOM
## *by* TANG PEI-SUNG

Demy 8vo.                                                        12*s*. 6*d*. net

"This delightful series of essays is the work of a man whose varied
experiences of life in China, Japan and the United States . . . have
left him still an undaunted biologist and research worker and above
all a Chinese. The essays can be enjoyed by anyone with an interest
in, and a speaking acquaintance with, modern science in the realms
of physiology and general biology, and they may also be read with
advantage by any specialist; for as might be expected from the land
of Confucius, an underlying unifying philosophy runs through
them."—*The Lancet.*

# BRITAIN'S GREEN MANTLE
## *by* A. G. TANSLEY

Demy 8vo.                                                        18*s*. net

"The present volume is an admirable introduction to the subject but it is also much more; it gives an attractive account of the wild plants of Britain in their natural setting, and is easily understandable by any reader who can distinguish an oak from an ash. . . . It is to be hoped that this book will be widely read, and that it may help to form a deep sense of responsibility for the safe-keeping of our rich and almost unique heritage. It is ours to enjoy, but not to despoil."
—Sir E. John Russell in *Sunday Times*.

"Dr. Tansley has done, in this new book, a telling service to the general reader by releasing his profound and encyclopaedic knowledge of British plant life and its history and ecology from its technical enclosure. It is a fine achievement to have succeeded so very readably as he has done."—H. J. Massingham in *Time and Tide*.


# INTRODUCTION TO PLANT ECOLOGY
## *by* A. G. TANSLEY

Lg. C. 8vo.                    Third Impression                    10*s*. 6*d*. net

"A standard elementary text-book on the subject has been needed for some time, and this book fills the gap admirably . . . a book which should be available to every teacher and student of the subject, whether at school or university."—*Times Educational Supplement*.


# PLANT ECOLOGY AND THE SCHOOL
## *by* A. G. TANSLEY and E. PRICE EVANS

Cr. 8vo.                                                         6*s*. net

# THE ELEMENTS OF GENETICS
## *by* C. D. DARLINGTON and K. MATHER

Demy 8vo.                    Second Impression                    30s. net

Genetics has undergone many transformations since it began with the rediscovery of Mendel in 1900. Drosophila and the chromosomes, population studies, human heredity and statistical methods, the chemistry of mutations and finally the great revelations of the genetics of micro-organisms have, each of them, meant a revolution in the study of heredity. The last has meant its combination with the study of development and infection also.

*The Elements of Genetics* by Darlington and Mather represents for the first time the whole length and breadth of this history. It is a concise text-book of genetics. But it is written by two workers who in their 15 years' collaboration have done as much as any others to make this new science. It is therefore bound to be a book for the research worker as well as for the student.

There are a great number of new figures, diagrams and tables, and a glossary with the authors' definitions of 500 terms gives clarity and precision to the whole work.

"Most stimulating, fascinating for the breadth of its ideas . . . a most important book of lasting value. . . . Packed with information and ideas from which all will profit and it should have the widest of publics."—*Eugenics Review*.


# GENES, PLANTS AND PEOPLE
## *by* C. D. DARLINGTON and K. MATHER

Demy 8vo.                                                         16s. net

Here is a collection of essays covering a large part of the field of genetics. They announce the generalizations and hypotheses developed over a period of twenty years during which they have served as some of the main signposts in the astonishing advance of this science. They deal with plants and animals, medicine and agriculture. They offer new interpretations of evolution, development and disease. Indeed they sketch out a rigorous framework of causation which is now being applied to the whole of biology.

GEORGE ALLEN AND UNWIN LTD

## THE SOILS OF PALESTINE
### *by* A. REIFENBERG

Demy 8vo.  Revised Second Edition  16*s*. net

For fifteen hundred years, because of erosion, the burning of dung and the destruction of ancient irrigation, the land "wherein thou shalt eat bread without scarceness, thou shalt not lack anything in it" has steadily deteriorated. If the new Jewish immigration is to restore the ancient fertility, it is obvious that the investigation of the properties of the soils of the country is a task of primary importance. In the following pages a description is given of soil formation within the framework of the Mediterranean type of weathering and at the same time an attempt is made to give a general survey of the soils of the country. This new edition records the progress made during the last ten years in the exploration of Palestinian soils and includes a short survey on the "Jordan Valley Authority." The chapters on the loess-soil of the Negeb, on peat and on fertilisers have been rewritten. New chapters dealing with the effects of saline irrigation water and with soil erosion have been added.

## SOILS: Their Origin, Constitution and Classification
### *by* GILBERT WOODING ROBINSON

Demy 8vo.  Third Revised and Enlarged Edition  35*s*. net

In the past twelve years the importance of this young branch of science has increased considerably with the public discussion of such topics as erosion and with the advances in our knowledge of the subject generally, in spite of the hampering of research by war conditions. Professor Robinson has, therefore, provided a complete revision of this now standard work (first published in 1932), in the light of this new knowledge. His book must be read by everyone in any way concerned with the soil—which today means the general reader as much as the advanced student.

## GEORGE ALLEN AND UNWIN LTD
are now the proprietors of Thomas Murby & Co

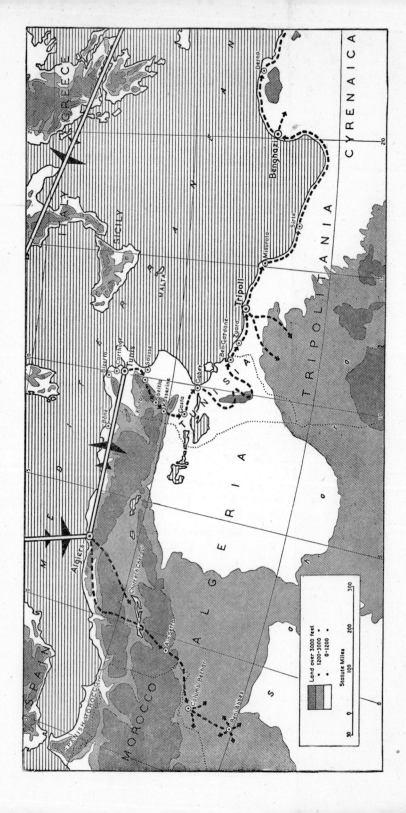